Diggers & Dreamers

THE GUIDE TO COMMUNAL LIVING
25th Anniversary Edition

Edited by

Chris Coates
James Dennis
Jonathan How

DIGGERS AND DREAMERS PUBLICATIONS

Diggers & Dreamers
Publications
2015

First published
2015
D&D Publications
BCM Edge
London
WC1N 3XX

ISBN-13
978-0-9545757-5-5
Paperback

Distribution
Edge of Time Ltd
BCM Edge
London
WC1N 3XX
020 8133 1451

Typesetting and Layout
Jonathan How

Acknowledgements: Thank you to all our contributors and to the many communities, housing co-ops and other organisations that have responded to our requests for information. We're very grateful to the places that have kindly hosted our editorial meetings over the last few years: Lammas, Birchwood, Redfield, Beech Hill, Mornington Grove, LILAC, Crabapple, Laurieston Hall, Neds Housing Co-op and Forgebank. We would also like to thank the communities which have generously donated towards the production of this book: Beech Hill, Birchwood, Brithdir Mawr, Canon Frome, Cornerstone, Coventry Peace House, Dol Llys Hall, Hockerton Housing Project, Laurieston Hall, Old Hall, Pendragon, Postlip Hall, Redfield, Share Instead and Tipi Valley.

Contents

Preface

Communal living is here to stay! It has been around for longer than anyone can remember and it shows every likelihood of having a place in whatever kind of future we're in for. Over the last quarter of a century *Diggers and Dreamers* has covered the ups and downs of those in the UK who have chosen this different way of life.

DIG: To move hard-packed earth out of the way. To take from the ground. A thrust; a poke – a dig in the ribs. To investigate, to research. An archaeological investigation. To understand or show interest in – "You dig?" To show appreciation – "Baby, I dig you".

Many of the communities listed in the first ever edition want to be included today. Others are still very much around but choose not to have an entry at the moment. A good scan through our back catalogue of directories shows a positive trend of communities having a long lifespan and, interestingly, a slow south-westerly migration!

In the following pages we have chosen both to celebrate some of those that have not quite got off the starting block as well as looking ahead to see what steps being taken to keep these valuable housing assets slipping back into the mainstream markets.

DREAM: Imaginary events seen in the mind while sleeping. A hope or wish. A condition or achievement that is longed for. To pass time idly or in reverie. To have a deep aspiration or hope, A visionary scheme; a wild conceit. To imagine: to conceive as possible.

We take a look at how a new co-operative town was planned; hear how we might, or might not, survive a collapse of society; ask 'what would a new UK eco-village look like?'; and explore how not to lose your housing co-op. Once you've had the dream of living communally you may need a bit of guidance so we finish off by giving you some pointers on becoming a member of an existing community.

So... some old dreams, some new dreams and some pointers on where and how to dig. Come along and join the kaleidoscope of people who have set out on the communal road. There really is a fairer way to live. Come and join us, digging and dreaming.

Owenstown:
A new co-operative community

JIM ARNOLD

*A new co-operative town in Scotland. A 21st century version of
Robert Owen's dream of villages of unity and co-operation.
A sustainable answer to the housing crisis.
What more could one wish for?*

This article examines the proposal to establish Owenstown, a new co-operative town, in the South of Scotland. The project takes an original 19th century co-operative idea from Robert Owen, the utopian socialist, and applies it to the modern age on an enlarged scale. The new town is located on a greenfield site in a rural area of economic and social deprivation caused by the decline of the coal mining industry. Current proposals are for 3200 homes and 8000 population. The background, the physical proposal, the motivation for the development of such a novel concept, and the process of implementation are examined below.

Background

Prior to retirement in 2010, I had spent most of my working life as the Director of a project for the restoration of the historic industrial village of New Lanark in Scotland, which is about 8km from the Owenstown site. New Lanark was founded in 1785 to spin cotton using the water power of the River Clyde, and with 2,500 inhabitants was one of the largest factories in the world during the period of the early industrial revolution. Production was maintained until 1968, when the factory closed and the village became derelict.

New Lanark Physical Link

New Lanark's restoration has been a source of inspiration for the Owenstown proposers. After the 1968 closure the village appeared to be doomed to demolition. A private, charitable, organisation, New Lanark Trust, was established in 1974 with public agency partnership support. Gradually the work to bring the village back to life realised success. Housing was restored and new people took up residence. The current population is about 150 in 65 households, and this represents a strong new community. The industrial buildings have been converted for other uses: a tourist facility which welcomes about 350,000 visitors per annum; a hotel with 38 bedrooms, eight self-catering cottages, and a leisure suite; and commercial offices and retail space. The Trust now employs around 165 people, and there are about 250 jobs in the village – which is about the same as when the mills closed in 1968. Many awards have been won, but perhaps the most significant recognition was in 2001 with the inscription of New Lanark on UNESCO's list of World Heritage Sites. As far as we know it is the only World Heritage Site with a utopian social element in its inscription.

For the proposers of Owenstown this process of resurrection has proved an inspirational example. Mostly, the proposers live locally in south/central Scotland. They watched the impossible resurrection happen, and this inspiration encouraged their actions. It provided them with an example of hope in an otherwise less than encouraging landscape.

Robert Owen

Specific inspiration was provided at an intellectual level by the philosophy of Robert Owen. When he arrived in New Lanark in 1800 as owner/manager he declared to a friend, "of all the places I have yet seen, I should prefer this in which to try an experiment I have long contemplated and wished to have an opportunity to put into practice"[1]. Under Owen's management many social experiments took place in the village, and Owen went on to become a working class hero. For a better understanding of this I refer you to a list of Owen's writings and related academic publications which is available at www.newlanark.org

The proposers of the new Owenstown were aware of the writings of Robert Owen. They were inspired by the writings and thoughts of this early industrialist, and prompted by them being on public display to visitors to his village. This provides a good example of the inspiration of a physical location. The ideal of utopia benefited from the existence of New Lanark as a surviving physical example of a particular philosophical view which is frequently difficult for the ordinary members of society to grasp, and in this particular case it also provided the stimulus for specific action.

Villages of Unity and Co-operation

There is an even more direct link, in that Owen had proposed the foundation of new "Villages of Co-operation" as a response to the problems of unemployment and distress in the post Napoleonic War period. As you would expect with Owen, he proposed a complete physical and philosophical package for his new village, and interestingly his ideas became more sophisticated over his lifetime. He thought that a population size of up to 2,000 was the optimum, which was similar to the size of New Lanark. The villages were to be economically and socially self sufficient, mainly based on industry and revolutionary agricultural techniques. Their architectural design and landscape setting was to be carefully controlled to provide a communal and positive environment, where the inhabitants would "unlearn many, almost all indeed, of the bad habits which the present defective arrangements of society have forced upon them: then, to give only the best

habits and dispositions to the rising generation, and thus withdraw those circumstances from society which separate man from man"[2]. Thus would Owen's New Moral World be realised by that revolutionary change of human personality created by these special utopian social arrangements.

Owen also dealt with financing and the economic return, "The expenditure will prove the greatest possible economy. Every shilling thus expended would be a national gain, create national improvement, find ample support for and remoralize the population employed, and return five per cent interest for the capital expended, leaving the property annually and rapidly increasing in intrinsic value."[2]

Hometown Foundation

This concept of creating a purpose designed new community to assist in overcoming the ills of contemporary society found a resonance 200 years later in the proposers of Owenstown. The Hometown Foundation Trustees represent a group of moderately wealthy Scottish businessmen who had been discussing social reform issues for some time, and had decided to investigate establishing a new community with the intention of creating a new social order in which individual members could actively demonstrate a more positive participation in every aspect of the community's structure. They considered that this was very like the change outlined by Robert Owen in his writings and in his proposals for Villages of Co-operation. The Hometown Foundation had bought

Owen's ideal community was drawn up in 1817 by the architect Stedman Whitwell. A large scale model was built and Owen used it on his lecture tours.

a farm of 820 hectares about 8 kilometres upstream from New Lanark village. This act of opportunism, to buy a potential village site, prompted them into further action and they have become progressively more committed to the proposal as they commissioned further consultancy work to examine the implications. A key element in the Hometown proposal has been that the land would be transferred at cost once planning approval was realised, thus allowing the infant community to capture the enhanced capital value.

The proposed size of the community in the first phase of approximately 10 years is 8,000 inhabitants. In recent times all new towns in Scotland, or the UK, of anything like this size have been established as a result of government policy and direct government intervention. No proposal for a new town is contained in the Scottish local government planning guidelines, which are very detailed and have just been revised. In contrast, with modern planning and government control of economic development, the proposal for Owenstown demonstrates the 19th century approach of the individual philanthropist. For contemporary Scotland it is as radical to propose a private sector new town, as it was for Robert Owen to make a similar proposal 200 years before.

Co-operation

In particular, Robert Owen was one of the founders of the Co-operative Movement, and the Hometown Foundation wanted to follow his example and set up Owenstown as a co-operative. The current definition of what constitutes a co-operative is conventionally from the International Co-operative Alliance, 'an autonomous association of persons united voluntarily to meet their common economic, social, and cultural needs and aspirations through jointly-owned and democratically-controlled enterprise.' Co-operatives are based on values of self-help, self-responsibility, democracy, equality, equity and solidarity. Co-operative members believe in ethical values of honesty, openness, and social responsibility.

Co-operative Development

My involvement in the Owenstown proposal was initially as the Village Director at New Lanark. I had never heard of the Hometown Foundation until their Chairman sat before me in my office and asked for help. He explained the general background of the Foundation, and how this had led to the purchase of land and development of a proposal for the establishment of a new co-operative town, and I could help by :

1. Agreeing that New Lanark should provide the venue for the launch of the Owenstown public consultation and holding a public exhibition which was to be part of the preparation for a formal planning application in. Planning law in Scotland had just been changed to require major projects to have a public consultation procedure prior to legal submission. This is designed to allow planning decisions to take into account representations as part of the development process.

2. Agreeing to become Chairman Designate of Owenstown Ltd, the operating company for the new town.

Refusal of these requests would have been difficult for any New Lanark Director. The opportunity to realise one of the dreams of Robert Owen and participate in the reform of society, the realisation of a landscape of hope, represented an irresistible vision. I did realise that my age meant that I could do nothing except help

Owenstown to achieve the first stages of realisation, but at least I might be able to help take those initial steps.

Co-operative Ethos and Planning

In November 2012 a formal application for planning permission in principle was submitted to the local government planning authority, which is South Lanarkshire Council. In the UK this is a complex and expensive process, even when it is 'in principle', and for Owenstown it cost nearly £1million. The planning submission is required to include items such as, sustainable urban drainage systems, structural and geophysical studies, economic and social impact studies, business plans, energy specifications including generation, supply and consumption, wildlife and ecological assessments, flood analysis, transport systems, services infrastructure, outline architectural designs for domestic dwellings and community facilities, and many other technical issues. The planning authority can ask for whatever information it considers 'reasonable', and it is a ground for refusal if it is not provided. It is a requirement that these technical elements will be analysed, planned, and constructed to the current highest standards, including general compliance with

government policies, such as carbon neutrality. The value of the initial ten year phase of works is currently estimated as approaching £500m. All of these costs are met by the co-operative development. There is no cost to the public purse. Business projections indicate that at the end of this ten year period the Owenstown co-operative will be financially sustainable.

My experience has been that as the voluntary and unpaid Chairman Designate of the operating company I attend the key meetings of the Owenstown Project Management Group. This is to ensure that the decisions which are being taken comply with the proposed social principles and that they will be practical to implement. The meetings are tough going, because the business is extensive and complex, and there is a small group of voluntary Trustees and a team of expensive paid consultants. There is constant tension between technical issues pragmatically required for a planning presentation and any visionary utopianism. Operational effectiveness was significantly enhanced in 2013 when a salaried project director post was established.

All this is what is required to establish a new community of a significant size in a developed west European state. A complex and expensive planning application and a detailed legal and financial structure have become unavoidable necessities. Small, very small, intentional communities could operate below the radar of officialdom and the state, though even here official regulation would be difficult to avoid. To achieve 'invisibility' they would have to fit into the existing structures, and unconformity would expose them to public inspection. Anything that is of a scale which is intended to achieve the reform of all society is almost unavoidably exposed to the full glare of officialdom. Robert Owen and the original Utopian Socialists did not have quite the same challenge.

Public Response

Some public response was received as a result of an initial public consultation in 2009-10 as part of the planning process, and the main conclusion was, "residents in the area were overwhelmingly positive about the proposed new settlement."[3].

One particular element reflects interestingly on the very issues which have been most difficult for the

Owenstown proposers. "Many were sceptical as to whether this (co-operative) concept would work. For some, it was difficult to imagine a way in which consensus could be agreed. While most understood the concept, they could not understand how the concept would work within a community of 8,000 homes"[4]. This view was picked up in later discussions and it was one of the reasons to scale back the proposals to an initial stage of 3000 homes and a population of 8000.

Rigside is an existing ex-mining village adjacent to the Owenstown site. Population is around 800, and on every social index it features discouragingly prominently as an example of acute rural social deprivation. Public support remained strong, including individuals coming up to us in the street and wishing us good luck, and members of the community attending the planning meetings and the eventual planning appeal.

All in support of Owenstown...

WHEN it comes to creating a new town of 20,000 inhabitants in the middle of the Clydesdale countryside, local folk are all for it. Well, almost all...

A survey has been taken to gauge public reaction to the ambitious scheme to create Owenstown, an environmentally friendly 21st century community on a site near Rigside.

And it shows an overwhelming, if qualified, welcome for the project.

Hometown Foundation officially launched the scheme with an exhibition at New Lanark, the cradle of modern, socially caring communities, cited as an inspiration for Owenstown.

As a follow-up to that launch, the Foundation commissioned a survey of people in South Lanarkshire to discover what they thought about the scheme.

With the promise of a healthy place to live in a rural setting with many leisure and social facilities, creating 8000 jobs to revive the Clydesdale economy, the obvious question in the survey would have been "What's not to like?"

And the findings published this week by Ipsos MORI show what Foundation spokesman, broadcaster Alan Douglas, describes as a "very postive" reaction.

Said Alan: "The telephone survey found that very few people envisaged any detrimental impact on them or their family and believed it would be an appealing place to work.

"The researchers said that investment on this scale has been very rare in the area and, therefore, interest from local people is high."

He admitted, however, that a minority of people surveyed worried that there might be some downside to Owenstown, especially the extra strain it might put on existing, stretched local services.

Owenstown, after all, will be Clydesdale's biggest single community with a bigger population than Carluke and twice that of Lanark.

Tempered

Said Alan: "Enthusiasm for the development was tempered only by some concerns about the pressure it might put on existing medical and sewerage services and it was felt more needed to be done to explain the concept of a co-operative community."

He said that some of those who might be Owenstown's first citizens had already come forward to express an interest in upping sticks and working and living in the new town.

Reasons why included finding a place with a better quality of life where there will be more facilities for young people, better job opportunities and, hopefully, a haven from crime and anti-social behaviour.

The survey results are being added to a dossier being compiled as part of a year-long public consultation exercise being conducted by the Foundation, which is a registered Scottish charity.

This evidence, once compiled, will form part of the final application for planning permission to get actual groundwork underway on the new town, Scotland's first in half a century.

It is expected that this application will go to South Lanarkshire Council in around a year's time.

Due to the sheer scale of the project, it is almost certain that the Scottish Government will become involved in the planning process at some point.

There has been a general welcome for the scheme from that direction already.

Meanwhile, the project seems to be attracting nationwide attention.

BBC Radio Four's rural magazine programme Open Country broadcast a feature on Owenstown on Saturday.

It will be repeated at 3pm on Thursday, November 12.

The BBC team interviewed some of the people behind the project, including the chairman of the Owenstown Co-operative Dr Jim Arnold.

RON HARRIS

Most seemed to feel that virtually nothing had happened in their village, and the surrounding ex coal mining villages of the Douglas Valley, since the mining closures of the 1950's. Owenstown offered them the prospect of a new initiative which was virtually certain to be beneficial for them.

In addition, there was general press support, and nearly 2000 expressions of interest were received from individuals and organisations, mostly via the internet. Most interest came from Scotland, but this was partially a reflection of the fact that the project was not generally publicised except in the local area, and publicity mainly related to the process of the planning application. Around half the people mentioned the co-operative community basis of the project as prompting their interest.

Co-operative Governance

How any new town will be governed and owned is not normally part of any planning application. It is treated by the planning authority as a completely separate, and not relevant, issue, but it became part of the initial conversation with council officials, and it presented interesting new challenges. The form of co-operative government proposed is unlike any other town in the UK. The works of Robert Owen were trawled for inspiration. Assistance was obtained from existing co-operative organisations: Co-operative Development Scotland, a government agency; and the Co-operative Enterprise Hub, which is a private sector organisation. Academic and legal opinion was invited. The result was that two documents relating to governance have been have been produced and included as part of the 2012 planning application. These are considered as drafts which will provide an initial foundation for the new community. They can be examined in detail by going to the South Lanarkshire Council planning website where they are included as part of the planning documentation. What they demonstrate is a preliminary framework, an outline mechanism, for the development of a new society.

Rules

The Owenstown draft company "Rules", which in UK law is the governing document for the new 'autonomous co-operative organisation', have been developed to a draft stage by a co-operative legal specialist, and are considered the current best statement of the legal possibilities. Essentially, the proposed structure sets up a democratically elected, community Board of Directors, with the wide legal powers required to establish, own, and operate a new town. This is the Board which will receive the land and related assets from the Hometown Foundation at cost. The resident community are the mutual owners and members, on nominal payment for a single shareholding. They elect the Board. Arrangements are made for the development of local area resident committees to ensure that the governing units are small and personal. Financial surpluses are returned to the community, with no individual profit. There are extensive provisions to prevent 'de-mutualisation' for private gain. There is also extensive provision requiring Directors to disclose any financial and other interests. It is this legal entity which will comprise the core of the Owenstown experiment

Masterplan

The extent of potential democratic control and co-operative activity has been investigated in a document which is a companion to the draft Rules, the 'Co-operative MasterPlan' (Draft). This has been prepared by a consultant expert and sits alongside all the other technical plans for Owenstown. At this stage the document crystallises the main social proposals to assist with the process of consultation and development. It does illustrate how potentially extensive is the principle of social co-operation. There is virtually no aspect of Owenstown life over which the residents cannot exercise positive influence. Absolute social control by a central committee is not a possibility, because the community is 'open', connected to the wider community, and residents have the capacity to change the structure, participate at various levels, or to leave. Dispute resolution is often an interesting issue for communities, and in this case formal resolution is available via the democratic processes associated with an annually elected governing committee.

Key elements of the co-operative enterprise include a building and construction company to create the new town, facilities and housing management, educational, training, and health facilities, social care, energy generation/distribution/supply, IT and communication services, financial services, leisure and recreational facilities, hotel and hospitality provisions, retail, transport, farming, property and industrial development, 'A co-operative culture would be built because people are involved in and receive services from different co-operatives every day of their lives'[5]. The MasterPlan identifies a series of 3 phases in which these organisations will require to be established. But it is not assumed that every individual will be a perfect social participant. The target in the MasterPlan is that around 20% of residents will be actively engaged in town governance, although virtually all would be members of some co-operative organisation. This approach illustrates that the co-operative model can be applied to most human socio-economic activities, and an inspection of the International Co-operative Alliance website, and their wide and varied membership, will easily illustrate how tenable is this view.

The Planning Hearing
and Political Support

The planning application was heard before the whole of South Lanarkshire Council at their meeting held on the morning of 1 April 2014. It took about two hours to rehearse the discussions which had been held with officials, and to answer Councillor questions. Then the Council accepted the recommendation of planning officials to reject the application, mainly on the grounds that it was outside the existing Local Development Plan and would be prejudicial to its implementation. There were also other grounds for objection relating to traffic and the environment. You can visit the council planning website to see (South Lanarkshire Council Planning Application ref CL/12/0530) the full details of the application and the rejection.

Social vision was not much in evidence during the planning hearing. The inspiration and expenditure represented by the Owenstown project had not enthused one single councillor to give support. Political enthusiasm from Hometown Trustees, and belief in a co-operative ideal, had not been enough.

Planning Appeal

Despite the unanimous rejection by the local authority it was decided to proceed with a Planning Appeal to Scottish Ministers. The feeling was that a different audience might be more sympathetic, and it might even expose the restricted view taken by the local authority in a different public forum.

A two day public hearing was held in a snowy January 2015, in the Community Hall in Rigside, the decaying mining village about 500 metres from the proposed Owenstown site. The procedure is that a Reporter is appointed by the Scottish Government, and he reviews the entire case, reports and makes recommendations to the relevant Minister. Planning matters are entirely devolved to Scotland. The procedure is that the appellant and the Council respond to specific questions which the Reporter has raised in advance with each of the parties. It is a fairly controlled but informal event, with a quasi-judicial flavour. South Lanarkshire Council defends its view and judgements. Owenstown appellants respond to the objections and make their case for the development. There is no inter-activity with the public audience.

The council fielded a 5-staff team, including a barrister. Over the two days Owenstown's team totalled 9, including co-operative, planning, legal, property, and economic and transport specialists. The cost to Owenstown exceeded £50,000, mainly in professional fees, and the discussion was often technical and detailed. Main areas of discussion were the Council's view that they did not believe the claimed economic benefits, or that the project could be achieved, and the planning legislation did not give them the capacity to control the co-operative element of the development, and it was prejudicial to their existing Local Development Plan, and there were major road transport objections. Owenstown reacted positively to every controversial issue, and the professional team produced a response which was as technically strong and as persuasive as anyone could imagine.

> **It requires that members of the community take control of their individual and social lives and actively participate in the creation of a new paradigm**

The Reporter collected his evidence, made a formal site visit, and it is likely that his recommendations and the related government decision will become available in 3-6 months. Support for Owenstown would be a radical development. It is much easier for the planning system to support the status quo and come to a conservative decision.

The Utopian Impulse

The aim of the Owenstown project is to achieve the creation of an exemplar community, and by creating a successful example to positively influence the way we structure society as a whole. It requires that members of the community take control of their individual and social lives and actively participate in the creation of a new paradigm. The plan is that the experiment should create one of the best and most interesting places to live in Scotland for the majority of the working population. I suspect it would be less inviting if an individual enjoys significant personal wealth and is required to accept democratic equality.

There are also some interesting aspects of Owenstown which reflect general issues in utopian thought.

For example, the Hometown Foundation avoids the use of the word 'utopian' for the reasons given by Ruth Levitas[6]... "the very term utopia suggests to most people that this dream of the good life is an impossible dream – an escapist fantasy, at best a pleasant but pointless entertainment...Colloquial usage thus tends to dismiss speculation about the good society as intrinsically impractical."

Another example is the idea of 'separation'. Utopians often consider it necessary to maintain their purity by being separate and different from existing society, and they create a physical and intellectual partition between themselves and their surrounding community. Usually the new community is proposed for a fresh rural location. For Owenstown this has been so strong that the proposers have vehemently resisted any proposals by the local authority that the development could be relocated to become a suburb of an existing settlement.

During this whole process, when even the administrative going has been tough, Hometown Trustees have shown no sign of wavering in their resolve to establish

this new community as a method to achieve the reform of existing society. Adversity appears to harden their determination and interest in finding effective solutions. They are a genuine reflection of the utopian impulse, the human search for a better form of society, identified by so many utopian writers.

The Next Stage?

Hometown Trustees have decided to wait to discover whether the Scottish national planning process will produce an approval for the currently proposed Owenstown site. Even if it does, the development and construction of a new village in the face of local authority opposition could prove very problematic. If a refusal is the outcome decision, a search for alternative sites will begin. Unsolicited interest has been expressed by a number of areas, including, for example, Ireland and Cambridgeshire, and preliminary contacts have been made.

From the initial experience of the last five years it is an obvious requirement that meaningful support from specific key politicians is an absolute necessity. Transferring to an alternative location would be dependent on meeting this fundamental provision. Without such support it would be very unlikely that any project of significant size could approach success. Owenstown showed that you needed to actually have a genuine desire to apply progressive concepts, and that unless there was such a pre-disposition there would be no inclination to meet the inevitable challenges. For politicians this is a very demanding prospect, with potentially overwhelming risk and deep involvement. Capitalist conservatism is a much more comfortable position.

Establishing a physical location for a new community is not an especially unusual project for property developers within our existing capitalist economic system. Each reader will probably already be aware of examples from their own local situation. However, each individual project is usually a long, complex, time consuming, expensive, controversial, and difficult occupation. The gestation period is frequently measured in decades. Property developers play a long and sophisticated game, usually motivated by the prospects of success and of spectacular financial reward. There is no obvious reason why any 'utopian' project

Dr J E Arnold *was Director of New Lanark between 1974 and 2010. From 2010 until 2015 he was Chairman Designate of Owenstown.*

should be any less arduous. They follow a similar development path, and there is no obvious reason why their route should be any smoother. In fact, the added philosophical dimensions of such a new proposal necessarily attach additional and problematic issues. The standard capitalist portfolio does not usually include new forms of community ownership and a restructuring of our economic and social systems. These, and the flexibility and requirement to have a capacity to accept change and necessary compromise, are extra and demanding parameters far beyond any standard development package. These projects are never going to be easy. Utopians have to be even tougher and more determined than developers.

1 Owen, Robert. *The Life of Robert Owen, Written by Himself 1857*

2 Owen, Robert. *The Plan for the Relief of the Manufacturing and Labouring Poor, 1817*

3 Owenstown – *Surrounding Residents Consultation Report, Ipsos MORI – 2010, page 12 – Initial Reaction*

4 Owenstown, *page 14 – Community Decision Making*

5 Hemmings, D. *Owenstown Co-operative MasterPlan, 2011*

6 Levitas, Ruth. *The Concept of Utopia, 1990*

• *If you are interested in finding more about Owenstown the easiest route is to visit the South Lanarkshire Council website (www. southlanarkshire.gov.uk). The reference for the Owenstown application is CL/12/0530.*

• *Hometown Foundation: hometown.co.uk*

• *Owenstown: www.owenstown.org*

In March 2015 a Scottish Government Reporter dismissed the appeal against the refusal of planning permission in principle for the Owenstown development in South Lanarkshire. The project may now be lost to Scotland altogether with other sites being looked at in England, Wales and Ireland. Its rejection raises concern from the Hometown Foundation that neither the planning nor political system is in tune with public opinion or the desires of individuals.

In his finding, the Reporter said he had to determine the appeal in accordance with the Council's development plan. Director Bill Nicol said: "Local people were all in favour of the development and councillors had no right to ignore their wishes by hiding behind minor planning matters which could have been easily resolved." According to opinion polls carried out on behalf of Owenstown's developers, there was overwhelming support for the project. Mori in particular said it was one of the clearest results they had ever seen.

"This represents a massive loss to the area and Scotland as a whole. We have spoken to authorities in England, Wales and Ireland about the concept and they have no difficulty understanding its potential," said Mr Nicol. We will now be investigating the opportunities that exist in other less blinkered parts of the country. What we can't understand is why our local and national elected representatives can't grasp something which is ambitious, visionary and morally right – perhaps it's because they didn't think of it first."

Trouble in Paradise

DYLAN EVANS

Would it be possible to survive a complete breakdown of society-as-we-know-it. From pretend apocalypse to Book of the Week on Radio 4, with a stop-off in a mental hospital along the way. For Dylan Evans it turned into quite a journey.

In 2006 I gave up my job, sold my house, and used the proceeds to set up a community in the Scottish Highlands. I knew from reading various accounts of previous communities, and visiting some currently existing ones, that it would not be easy. Still, nothing really prepared me for quite how difficult it would turn out to be.

My community was supposed to be different from many of the others I had read about and visited in two main ways. Firstly, it would be strictly temporary, lasting just eighteen months. Volunteers could stay for up to three months, but could also come for as little as two weeks.

Secondly, it was meant to be a simulation of life after the collapse of global civilization. We would try to figure out what life might be like if civilization collapsed, by acting as if it already had. It was to be a kind of collaborative storytelling, a real-life role-play. To this end, I sketched out an imaginary scenario, explaining how our twenty-first century high-tech civilization might collapse under the weight of climate change, peak oil, and economic instability. All the volunteers were supposed to read this scenario before they arrived. Then we would continue the story, not by merely imagining what would happen next, but by acting it out in the real world.

It was great to begin with. When I first arrived on site it was summer, and it was fun to spend the long warm days outside chopping wood, clearing the land for the crops, and setting up our yurts. But we soon began to face plenty of problems.

1 Growing enough food

Like many other communities, we aimed to become self-sufficient, at least in terms of vegetables. We also kept chickens and a few pigs, which we occasionally killed to make bacon, sausages, and smoked ham. We didn't have enough land to keep a cow, but we occasionally traded our eggs for some milk from a local farmer. But it takes months to prepare the land, plant crops, and take care of them until harvest time. In the mean time, we had to make regular runs to the supermarket.

If you are simply aiming to set up a commune, this is no big deal. But if you are trying to simulate life after the collapse of civilization, it is galling. At first I had justified these shopping trips, in terms of our scenario, by arguing that in the immediate aftermath of a global catastrophe, the survivors would be able to scavenge supplies from local houses and abandoned shops. But the grace period offered by the leftovers of civilization would only last so long, and the survivors would have to make sure they could grow or catch all their own food by the time the packaged stuff ran out. When we were still making trips to the supermarket a year into the experiment, I began to wonder how valid our simulation really was.

And after a while, the hard work of digging and planting and weeding stops being fun and becomes tedious and exhausting. It's one thing to do it for a week or two, as a kind of occupational therapy, but when you have to do it day in day out, you can find yourself yearning for the easy life of an urban consumer once again.

2 Keeping warm and dry

Our accommodation at Utopia consisted largely of home-made yurts. These elaborate tents are perfectly suited for the harsh Mongolian climate. A stove in the middle is kept burning day and night, while thick layers of felt trap the warmth inside and make it nice and snug. That, I thought, would be vital in the Scottish winter. But, as I would be reminded, frequently, Scotland is not just cold. It is also wet – much wetter, in fact, than Mongolia. And though our yurts had an extra layer of rough canvas on top of the felt, this was not enough to keep out the kind of persistent, unrelenting rainfall that makes Scotland such a difficult place to live.

A considerable amount of our time in the Utopia Experiment was, therefore, spent trying to keep the rain out of our yurts. This did not make for particularly pleasant sleeping conditions. Often I would drowse off warm and dry, the stove burning and the canvas firmly tied down, only to awake in the dead of night, bitterly cold, to find the stove had gone out and the rain was dripping through gaps in the canvas that had been fumbled open by the wind. I would lie shivering in my sleeping bag, unwilling to get out and tie the canvas back down for fear of getting even colder and wetter, cursing my decision to build those bloody yurts.

3 Running out of money

When enthusiasts and idealists wax lyrical about community life, the question of money is often glossed over. Yet communities can only survive if they have a sound economic basis. I funded the Utopia Experiment entirely out of my own pocket, using the profit I made from selling my house. Nevertheless, we still ran out of money before the experiment was due to end, as I had badly underestimated how much it would all cost, and we wasted a lot of the money on useless stuff, like a solar panel that only generated enough electricity to keep a single light bulb going for a couple of hours a day.

Within a few months, I began to worry not only about how I would be able to keep the experiment going, but also about what on earth I would do after it was all over. I wondered if I would end up homeless, and whether I would ever be able to get another job. These worries played on my mind and made me increasingly gloomy, but they didn't affect the volunteers, who could all go back to their former lives when they left the site.

4 Personal investment

The founder of another community in Scotland was puzzled by the fact that I was funding everything out of my own pocket. He thought it smacked of desperation, as if I was trying to "buy friends," as he put it. Be that as it may, the fact that the volunteers didn't have to contribute financially meant that they had less personal investment in the success of the experiment.

Also, I began to realize that the time-limited nature of the experiment itself contributed to this problem. Why start a big project like this and then abandon it after just a couple of growing seasons? If people could come along for just a month, how would they be motivated to work hard for a harvest they wouldn't reap?

5 Social tensions

In all the classic descriptions of utopia, from Thomas More's 1516 account to the 1890 novel by William Morris, News from Nowhere, harmony reigns. There is no social tension, and everyone gets along famously. I set out with a similarly rosy view of how the community would function. I pictured a harmonious group of fellow survivors, all glowing with affection for one another.

Of course, things turned out rather differently. One or two people didn't pull their weight, and this got on everyone else's nerves. Worst of all, I discovered I didn't really like being around a bunch of strangers. I was used to spending a lot of my time alone, and I hated the lack of privacy.

Small communities are like pressure cookers, with no relief valve. Tensions are exacerbated when you rub shoulders with the same few people all day every day. It is one thing to live in a large extended family group, as our ancestors did before they started farming, and quite another to spend all your time with strangers, with little opportunity to escape from those you dis-like. Jealousy and resentment find fertile soil in such confined spaces.

Most people were happy to follow the rules we devised, but one person in particular seemed determined to do his own thing. For example, he never used the compost toilet, preferring to dig a new hole every time he felt like having a crap. At one point I calculated that if all the volunteers behaved like that, then by the end of the experiment the site would be covered by ten thousand little mounds, each containing a single turd. Clearly this was not ecologically sustainable.

6 Planning permission

About ten months into the experiment, I got a letter from the Area Planning and Building Standards Manager at the Highland Council. 'During a recent visit,' it said, 'it became apparent that development has commenced prior to the granting of planning permission.' The letter also asked me to 'halt all works on site' until such permission was granted. 'Failure to do so,' it concluded, 'may result in formal enforcement action being taken against you.'

Apparently I needed to apply for permission to put up the yurts, and to convert the Barn into a kitchen and dining area. This seemed bizarre to me, given that none of this was permanent, and we'd be taking everything away when the experiment came to an end the following year. But that was the law, and I began to worry that officials might descend on Utopia at any time, and shut the experiment down.

And so I began the lengthy process of applying for planning permission. This involved filling out numerous forms, taking photographs, and producing scale drawings of the yurts and other structures we were building. The irony of jumping through so many bureaucratic hoops in order to pursue an experiment in primitive living didn't escape me. But it didn't amuse me either. One of the biggest attractions about the experiment had been the promise of a life free from paperwork. And now I was drowning in it.

7 I went mad

Beyond all the practical difficulties of growing food, running out of money, and so on, the biggest problem in the Utopia Experiment was me. To cut a long story short, I went mad, and ended up in a psychiatric hospital. This must have come as quite a shock to the volunteers, who mostly seemed to enjoy their time at the experiment, and worked hard to make it a success. One of them later wrote that they felt let down when, as time wound on and I became increasingly depressed, I would only appear "apparition-like, fleetingly and uselessly, before disappearing again without notice."

My presence, he added, began to demoralize people. The volunteers wanted me to be an active, engaged and productive member of the group, but I was increasingly incapable and incompetent.

When I came out of hospital, I went back to Utopia and told everyone that the experiment was over. I had expected them all to simply pack up and leave. But they didn't want to go. And there was nothing I could do about that. So eventually I just left them to it. Later, I learned that they had renamed the community the Phoenix Experiment, reflecting their view that it had risen from the ashes of Utopia. The last I heard, some of them were still there.

Success or failure?

So, was my experiment a success or a failure? For a long time, it felt like a complete disaster to me. I hadn't achieved any of my original ambitions. I had not transformed myself into a strapping backwoodsman. We had failed to grow enough crops to feed ourselves. We had run out of money and squabbled like surly children. And to cap it all, I had ended up in a mental hospital.

Looking back on it now, though, I can see that it was in many ways a success. The volunteers largely enjoyed their time at Utopia, and today there is still a thriving vegetable garden with a community-funded poly-tunnel. I learned some hard lessons about life and about myself. And while my dream may have turned into a nightmare, at least I followed it. I won't sit around in my old age, wondering what would have happened if I had put that crazy plan into action, instead of carrying on with my job as a university lecturer.

However, if I were to ever try something like this again, there are several things I would do differently.

First and foremost, I would do it somewhere warm. Doing the experiment in Scotland was a great way to challenge myself, but it did get very cold and wet, and the long dark winter nights were bleak and depressing. A Mexican beach would be much more pleasant.

Second, I would do it with friends, not a bunch of strangers. Or I might even do it all on my own, like Thoreau did at Walden Pond. Then it wouldn't be a community of course, but one of the things I discovered in Utopia was that I actually prefer to spend most of my time alone.

Third, if I did do it with other people, I would insist that they all had to invest some of their own funds in the experiment, so that they felt that they had a personal stake, and risked some of their own money on it.

Fourth, I would do some detailed financial planning before I started, and make sure I had an ongoing income stream to keep things going throughout the experiment.

Fifth, I wouldn't aim to become self-sufficient. I would be extremely selective about what I tried to grow, and not worry about having to go the shops to buy the rest.

Sixth, I would have an exit strategy. I would have a plan B in case it all went wrong, and I decided I no longer wanted to be there. But I wouldn't set an end date in advance, so it could go on as long as people wanted it to.

Last but not least, it wouldn't be based on a post-apocalyptic theme. We wouldn't try to act out any kind of scenario. We would just do it for fun.

Author bio:
Dylan Evans has written several popular science books, including Introducing Evolutionary Psychology, which was required reading for the actors in The Matrix trilogy. and set up two companies. His latest book is The Utopia Experiment (Picador, 2015).

Ecoville 2000

TONY GOSLING
& CHRIS COATES

Why is it so difficult to create an eco-village in the UK? What would a fully sustainable eco-village look like? At the very end of the 20th century the Centre for Alternative Technology tried to answer these questions and looked at how the idea might be implemented in the middle of France.

> "Gerard Morgan-Grenville appeared at CAT and said he wanted to talk to me about a new idea he had got and his great new idea was, to put it in a nutshell, to mainstream the idea of ecovillages. In other words he felt that there were some fantastic things about the concept of ecovillages, but it was to some extent, in his view, hamstrung by the fact that the majority of the people involved in them had no money, no resources, they had to start very small and they tended to grow very slowly... he felt it had to be taken up a few rungs and approached in a 100% professional way, but without compromising any of the ideals of the concept of an ecovillage."
> Roger Kelly[1]

The idea of setting up an alternative village scale intentional community somewhere in the UK has been around for a long time. Back in the seventies attempts were made by a number of different groups to get a large scale community off the ground. A couple of these attempts were to establish a community in the abandoned quarry village of Porth y Nant, on the Llyn Peninsula, in North Wales. Initially a group calling themselves the New Atlantis Commune squatted the site; later a proposal was put forward to buy the village by Nicholas Saunders who had stumbled across it while researching his *Alternative England & Wales* book.

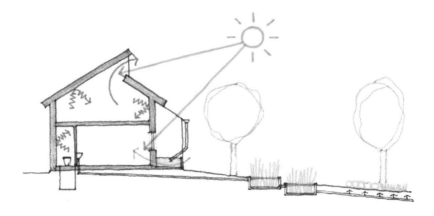

Following a number of Free Festivals (called the Meigan Fayres) held between 1973 and 1975, a group formed hoping to set up a community on the site of the run down Penlan Holiday Village at Cenarth, further down the Welsh coast in Pembrokeshire. Serious proposals were put forward in 1976 by a group calling itself the 'The Association for the Development of a Craft Village and Centre for Charities' to transform over 200 large wooden barrack buildings at the Park Hall Army Camp outside Oswestry in Shropshire into a village sized community. A planning application submitted to turn the 260 acre army base into a craft village was eventually turned down.

In 1974 a number of people keen to see the formation of new rural communities had formed the New Villages Association with the stated aim: 'to demonstrate the practicability and desirability of such an alternative, by establishing self-sufficient New Villages to provide the basis for a sustainable and more hopeful society.' The group initiated a 'New Villages viability study' to work out how much land a village would need to support itself. While the original thrust of the Association had been the establishment of actual self-sufficient villages and it had been assumed that this could be done by simply finding participants, a site and the necessary capital and that "organisation would develop naturally from the participants." This turned out to be easier said than done and the Association turned more and more to being a research organisation. Two of the stalwarts of the group, Lin and Don Warren, moved to a small site at Cleeve Prior near Evesham and set up the Food and Energy Research Centre to carry out practical research in self-sufficiency – albeit on a small scale – to test the ideas that were being generated by the viability study. The Association carried on into the early 1980's producing newsletters and carrying out research into planning problems, finance schemes and past co-operative ventures. In the end they concluded that it was "clear that no New Village could be set up without some involvement by local, and probably central, government..." and saw their role as trying to demonstrate that there was a need for new villages, drawing up detailed plans to show that a New Village would actually work and "...that it really is possible for people to supply their needs from a fair share of land without large inputs of resources."

Delegates to the 1976 United Nations 'Habitat' conference on human settlement in Vancouver were shown detailed plans developed by the former Leicester City Council planner Konrad Smigielski for an 'Evolutionary Village' in the grounds of the Co-operative College at Stanford Hall near Loughborough. The plans were for a self-supporting co-operative village with a population of about 2000 people utilising 80 acres of parkland surrounding Stanford Hall to build a village of a 1000 houses with "Carp farming on an existing 3 acre lake, a furniture factory and a cheese making factory..." In his address to the conference Smigielski stated he was convinced that "in 10 years time there will be such a village!"

By the time Gerard Morgan-Grenville[2] walked into Roger Kelly's office at the Centre for Alternative Technology(CAT) in the early 1990's, and put forward his great idea to 'mainstream ecovillages', no village scale intentional community in the UK had made it off the drawing board and into reality. Roger Kelly was reluctant to take up the idea, but Morgan-Grenville was persistent and kept badgering Roger with his latest thoughts and ideas. Eventually stating "The conclusion I've come to is that this isn't going to happen in the UK. It's just impossible. There's this combination of ridiculous land values, ridiculous planning laws, terrible bureaucracy. Everything militates against doing something like this in the UK." Suggesting that the best first step would be to set up a prototype ecovillage somewhere in Europe and then to later bring the idea back to Britain.

Roger was persuaded to join the former brigadier on a whirlwind tour of abandoned villages in the north of Spain where the two men tried to find a site and a sympathetic local government body. Drawing a blank in Spain Morgan-Grenville used his contacts in France to get access to the office of President Mitterrand whereupon he persuaded the French President that what he had got to do was an Ecovillage development. The French government then offered to facilitate finding a suitable site in France. The condition was that a feasibility study (proving that the idea was both practically and economically viable) was carried out. They were prepared to pay for this. There followed an eco-tour-de-France looking at several sites being suggested by regional authorities. All of these, for one reason or another (high voltage cables across the land, ex-military base with nuclear bunkers...), were deemed unsuitable.

Eventually an 850 hectare tract of land at Versels, in the Lozère department in the Languedoc-Roussillon region, was identified. It was currently being used as a wild boar hunting reserve and the owner wished to sell. Using this possible site as a basis for the feasibility study Roger Kelly agreed to take on the project and CAT embarked on an 18 month study into what scale an ecovillage would need to have in order to be viable as well as how one would go about setting it up.

Quite how to go about working out what a fully-fledged eco-village would look like was not immediately obvious – there was no place to go and look up what constituted a fully sustainable community. As well as working with the team at CAT and drawing on as much existing experience from other intentional communities that he could find Roger teamed up with a former CAT worker Richard St George[3] who had recently become the Director of the Schumacher Society and had been working on a project for the Society on how to make the village of Chew Magna, in Somerset the "Greenest village in England".

Roger and Richard had both been racking their brains over a dilemma. Small ecological communities might be acting as beacons for future sustainable development, but pioneering communities needed to be bigger to make an impact. The question was how big?

Diagramatic plan of south end of site

— Public road
— Private vehicular road
— Pedestrian/cycling route
☐ Parking area
● Village centre
● Residential neighbourhood
● Eco-gîtes development
● Light Industrial development

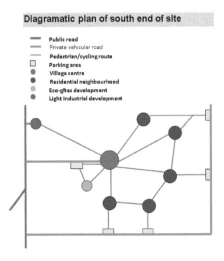

The fundamental test of a community's viability, Richard concluded, was its ability to retain its young people and enable people of all ages to share positions of responsibility. Too many young people brought up in intentional communities were fleeing the nest. What would keep them there would be a standard of living as good as or better than the best civilisation has to offer combined with an independent spirit. In the winter of 1994 Richard woke one morning to find himself snowed in and unable to get into work at CAT. A good time he decided, to tackle the issue that had been bugging him. He sat down and began to list every service that we might expect in any civilized community; doctor, farmer, teacher, mechanic, builder, plumber, carpenter, printer, IT fixer, and the list went on. Eventually it ran to over 220 roles under eleven headings: agricultural; crafts; arts; sports; estate management; services; health; educations; commercial; technical; and industrial. Each role would need from between one and 25 people to fill it. The number of individuals needed to fulfil these essential roles panned out at 600. But a

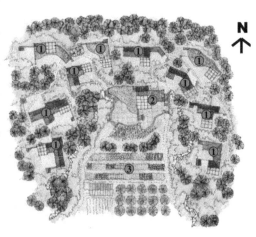

N
↑

significant percentage of the community were likely to consist of 'dependents'; for example children, the elderly, infirm or sick, drop-outs, youths at university, pregnant and nursing mothers, and people on holiday or secondments. When Richard eventually arrived back for work at CAT he announced the magic number for viability to be 1000 people.

Over the next 18 months the team at CAT worked on the details of what became known as Ecoville 2000. This included an in depth analysis of the site at Versels, in the high reaches of the Masif Central. Covering: the geography of the site; weather and climate conditions; soil composition and vegetation; existing population(or lack of); current community facilities; communication and transport links; and the potential for renewable energy generation on the site.

Roger was working on designs for the Ecohomes. People tend to like living close to other families but not to too many, and he settled on an ideal cluster of ten to twenty houses, with each being up to a kilometre from the village centre. Each cluster had individual houses, most with attached workshops, a building with communal facilities, such as laundry, meeting room, boilerhouse or store for shared tools and equipment; and an area of horticultural land, for residents' own needs but also selling surplus produce. The core of the design was a village square built around existing farmhouses and other buildings and compromising workshops and exhibition space, a cafe/bar, a small shop etc.

> **People tend to like living close to other families but not to too many**

The study also contained profiles of various intentional communities from around the globe from Crystal Waters in Australia through Lebensgarten in Germany, The Gyurufu Foundation in Hungary, The Farm in Tennessee and the Findhorn community in Scotland.

At this point the project shuddered to an ignominious halt as the farmer's sons changed his mind and his father decided to keep the land. Roger describes the change of heart as sickening, all their time and effort had come to nothing. This was too much for the team and it brought Ecoville 2000 to a halt. Nowhere has Ecovillage 2000 received the recognition it deserves for attempting to merge top flight ecological and social models with 21st century technologies. The late 1990's were the very early days of digital publishing and no electronic version of the completed feasibility study exists. Roger Kelly had a few paper copies which over the intervening years he has given away to interested folk. Copies presumably exist somewhere in the archives at CAT or in the files of some French Ministry somewhere, but attempts we have made to track them down have not turned up anything. (If anyone reading this has a copy gathering dust on their shelves please let us know – via *Diggers & Dreamers*.) Details in this article were put together from interviews with Roger and Richard and material from the original feasibility study files kindly shared with the authors by Roger.

Tony Gosling *is an ex BBC researcher and investigative journalist who lives in Bristol. He has been on the National Executive of the National Union of Journalists. He helped establish Ecovillage Network UK.*

Two decades on from its inception we need a development along the lines of Ecovillage 2000 more than ever before. As some kind of answer to our impending environmental crisis, energy crisis and housing crisis. If we lived in a country that was serious about addressing these issues we would see proposals along these lines coming forward from the government as planning policy. But despite the work done by CAT, the New Villages Association before them and today the work of GEN (Global Ecovillages Network) the establishment of a truly sustainable new village scale settlement in the UK still looks a long way off.

"If you're looking for solutions you can get half way there by tinkering with the technology or you can get half way there by changing your cultural solutions. To get 100% there you have to have to add the technical change and the cultural change together... It'll happen, it's not if, it's only a question of when it'll happen. But I think we might soon be looking at a new movement to build new villages on ecological principles..."
Richard St George

1 *Roger Kelly was a housing association pioneer in the 1970s. As founding director of Solon South West he built and managed thousands of homes in the South West of England before moving to Wales to become director of the Centre for Alternative Technology (CAT) in 1988.*

2 *Gerard Morgan-Grenville was great-grandson of the last Duke of Buckingham. He graduated from Eton into the early environmental movement via the army and an early career renting out barges for luxury holidays in France. He was the founder of CAT and later co-founded the Green Alliance with Maurice Ash. In 1983, he was appointed a Countryside Commissioner, first for England and then for Wales. He died in 2009.*

3 *Richard St George was an early director and later Trustee at CAT. An interest in fish culture led to a job on the Pacific island of Tuvalu in the late 70's and on returning to the UK he set up Low Energy and Solar Supplies, one of the UK's early solar companies. From the mid-90s until 2009 he was Director of the Schumacher Society. He died in 2012.*

Some sections of this article previously appeared in:

• *Gosling, Tony. Ecoville, The Land Spring, 2007*

• *Coates, Chris. Communes Britannica, D&D Publications, 2012*

In the beginning...

CHRIS COATES

The Genesis Project had the kind of attributes that intentional communities always have in movies: a logo, a 152-page bound paperback "proposal", "carefully selected" participants, people scouring the planet for potential sites... the members would have probably worn really cool uniforms as well!

In October and November 1975 one thousand carefully selected individuals and organisations received copies of a prospectus for a new community for 200 people in a location yet to be decided, but possibly in Southern Ireland, Wales, Southern England or New Zealand. The Genesis Community project was the brainchild of Lindsay Rawlings a former Gurkha, stockbroker and swinging London restaurant owner who had had a life-changing moment on reading an article in *The Observer* entitled Spaceship Earth.

"...It outlined many of the things which he considered likely to go wrong for this planet between now and the turn of the century, and I was astonished. It took me six months of research and thought to confirm in my own mind the realities of the global situation; and it was during these months that my interest in 'communities' was first aroused..."
Lindsay Rawlings, Genesis Proposal

Over the next couple of years Rawlings discussed the possibility of setting up a community with a group of his London friends and in January 1974 they started

Lindsay Rawlings

to meet weekly to discuss and plan the project in detail. After spending the summer of 1974 touring communities in England, Scotland, France and Belgium Rawlings spent the rest of the year putting together the first draft of the *Genesis Proposal* and "planning how it should be brought to the notice of those who are most likely to contribute to its success." At the same time he sold his restaurants and on New Year's Day 1975 cropped his hair "a symbolic clearing of the decks for action," and set off to scout for a site for the new community. Flying to Australia and on to New Zealand while another member searched among various islands in the Indian Ocean for a suitable location and one of Rawlings' brothers drove the length of South America, from Tierra del Fuego to Mexico, keeping his eye out for a site. Following this grand tour the finishing touches were put to the 160 odd page *Genesis Proposal* and an initial print run of 1000 produced and mailed out to contacts the group had made across Europe, the United States and Australasia. These included some 300 people who the group already knew, several hundred others who had become interested in the project and who had answered an elaborate questionnaire that the group had sent out to anyone expressing an interest in the project and others who received the document out of the blue. A further 500 copies were printed in December 1975 to meet the interest generated by a series of adverts placed in alternative magazines in the UK and USA, newspapers such as the *International Herald Tribune, The New Zealand News, The Times* and *The Observer.*

The Genesis Proposal is a remarkable document. While on the one hand it states that nothing is fixed and how the community will work will be decided by those who eventually live in it, it sets out in expansive detail everything from a community Behaviour Code, Design and Construction details, draft community Byelaws, policies on pets and working animals through to community rituals/traditions/routines and celebrations. The proposal sets out to be a visionary document for a new way of living.

"The community which we are in the process of creating will be a rural one, with all the land and

materials that we need for producing our own food and energy. As far as is possible it will be self-sufficient. It will have a great feeling of privacy, of domain, and yet will be within fairly easy reach of major centres of population. It will provide for considerable interaction with the 'outside world'. It will be simple but comfortable. In some ways it will be very sophisticated. Its members and those passing through it will find in it outstanding opportunities for self-development and spiritual growth. It is likely to appeal to a wide cross-section of people, including many who might not ordinarily have thought of being part of a community. It is going to have to provide cumulatively more of what matters in life to its members than they might find elsewhere, or there will be little point in their being there. It will be a 'light centre' in its particular corner of the globe."

This is set against an almost apocalyptic vision of the future:

"...the world situation, already unbelievably serious (unbelievable by some people), will in the foreseeable future reach catastrophic proportions (although I do not regard what is happening as catastrophic). I am not talking about the way that things have always been, extremely tough for some and very tough for most of the others. I am talking about globally inter-related problems so serious that our complete ecosystem, our life-support systems, systems of government, of exchange, of communication will collapse or erupt on a scale never before experienced by humankind. I am talking about destruction and disruption, social and physical, which will make World War II or the great floods or plagues of history look like the limited affairs which by comparison they were."

Genesis Proposal

GENESIS

New Age Community

THE GENESIS COMMUNITY is being born. A detailed proposal defining the community will go out in July to upwards of 300 very carefully chosen people, all of whom are significant to the project and most of whom have expressed considerable interest in Genesis during the last 12 months.

It will be on the strength of this proposal that some of these will come together as founder members of the community at a remarkable gathering in November 1975. Approximately five months later some of us will move on site (almost certainly in either New Zealand or Southern Ireland) to start building a new age community the like of which has not been seen before, one providing every imaginable opportunity for human and spiritual growth.

It seems that we have the capacity to do this. Genesis is showing signs of being part community, part network of people, with locations in Australasia, the United States and Britain.

If you are interested in what we are doing, write to us briefly enclosing return postage. We shall ask you to answer a very searching questionnaire before sharing our elaborate plans further. Keep flowing! Keep growing! We love you:
The Genesis Community,
BM-Genesis,
London WC1V 6XX

GENESIS

The appendices of the proposal contained various articles and writings that had influenced and inspired Rawlings to conceive of the project. A comprehensive timetable is laid out for the setting up of the community. Starting with Phase I – the Formation Period: to March 1976 which included the core team meeting with those interested in the project and concluded with The Gathering:

"The Gathering will be a special 14-day 'workshop', carefully designed for Genesis. It is something in which relatively few interested people will be invited to take part. It will provide participants with a very 'safe' space in which to meet themselves and each other and to look at their futures together. We will be working through the proposal, discovering our group consciousness on a host of different issues. We will be working together and playing together. Some of us may be meeting others more closely than they have ever met anybody before. Between us we will be establishing the norms and setting the pace for the future community. The Gathering is likely to be an incomparable experience, not to be missed by anyone who is eligible to be there – to the extent that almost no barrier should stand in the way."

During Phase II, the 'Countdown Period', it was envisaged that members would be "phasing themselves out of their current work and home situations, liquidating assets and generally preparing themselves for the move into community and for the very different life that lies ahead." While some would be locating and arranging to purchase the community's land in advance of the group

SIZE

13

116   The community will be designed and laid out from the start for about two hundred people, including perhaps fifty of our children and some thirty scheduled visitors at any one time. Our building programme will start with these figures in mind.

117   The number which we will need to found the community is somewhere upwards of a dozen. There may be a limit to how many we can accommodate on an undeveloped site whilst clearing and construction work is in progress, but that is a problem which we will face if it arises.

118   If it seems right at any point to halt membership, then that is what we shall do. It seems likely that if the community is what its early members intend it to be; it will continue to attract members long after we have exhausted our capacity to absorb them. As the community takes shape it will become increasingly easy for people to identify with and choose the way of life which a flourishing community provides.

119   There are likely to come points at which we shall decide to branch out. A group consisting of some old and some new members might choose to establish themselves a few miles up the valley from our original site, there to live separately from, but in close contact with, the original community. In time, groups will split and establish similar communities in other parts of the world, possibly with different emphasis. I hope so.

120   It is important that the community be large enough to provide its members with a wide range of social contacts and access to abundant knowledge and skills, whilst enabling us still to maintain close and loving contact with each other. If the community feels crowded with seventy-five members, we can do something about it. If it still feels good as we top two hundred and fifty, then I expect we shall keep growing.

121   Our Behaviour Code, our attitudes as a community, our clear thinking and our attunement to the inner and to each other will go a long way towards helping us overcome the innumerable problems to which large groups are prone. We do have the means to live fulfilled lives together.

☐

Chinese house of the Sung Period

moving in. The hope was that by perhaps September 1976 at the earliest or sometime before 1978 at the latest a site would have been purchased and the community ready to start. This would be the trigger for Phase III, the building period, during which the community infrastructure would be realised: renovation of buildings, construction of new buildings "creating access tracks, laying down services, breaking in new land, not to speak of breaking in ourselves"

The publication of the proposal elicited responses from the UK and abroad and a date was set for an 18-day Gathering at a large house in Beddgelert in North Wales. On 25 April 1976 thirty-two would be participants in the project met for the first time. Some had travelled from the USA, Canada, Australia and New Zealand. Over an intense fortnight the group explored their personal visions of the community and their responses to the proposal. Two of the days were led by Swedish Architect-planner Johannes Olivegren and Michael Shaw and Martin Vance from Findhorn. The proceedings were written up and simultaneously projected on to an overhead screen.

"There was singing, tears, laughter, sickness, joy and elation and individual times of doubt and sadness. We could hardly have hoped for more. One of the few actual decisions which we felt it necessary to reach was to buy a very large property somewhere in the British Isles as our initial base, one in which to centre ourselves before expanding into further sites in the United Kingdom and abroad."
Genesis Open Letter 1 July 1976

A small group spent a few weeks in the summer of 1976 looking at a dozen or so large properties across the Britain from a list of 50 they had got the particulars for – "none with less than 35 bedrooms." By September they had started negotiating to buy Manderston, a huge 56 bedroom house and grounds in the Borders near the town of Duns. Through their Findhorn connections they were offered a 'winter-let' of the Argyll Hotel on the Scottish Island of Iona and on 11th October twelve adults and two children made their way to Iona, via the first week-long conference at Findhorn "The World Crisis and the Wholeness of Life" – with David Spangler and E F Schumacher. While the newly formed Genesis group got busy working out the mechanics of communal living Lindsay Rawlings spent the last months of 1976 visiting British Colombia to meet with Lord Martin Cecil and his son Michael,

NATIONALITY/RELIGION/POLITICS

199

25

This will be a multi-national, undenominational community with no political affiliations. As far as we are concerned neither race nor creed nor political leanings will ever of *themselves* be barriers to membership of the community.

Origins

200

The community will have originated in England and its initial membership will have been drawn from the United Kingdom and the United States, with much smaller numbers coming from the Continent, from New Zealand, Australia and elsewhere. The main language of the community will inevitably be English.

Religion

201

As a community our credo will be that all Gods and all ways to God are one. We will hope to provide the space for each of us to travel by whatever routes we choose, provided that those routes in no way impede the passage of others. Genesis will *not* provide the space for any *one* way to be presented as the *only* way. If, for instance, 'the Christian way' or Yogi Poppadum's teachings or any other creed or path is what it is *all* about for you — to the exclusion of all other possibilities — then that will be fine by the community *at the same time as being unsupportable by the community.*

Politics

202

As a community we shall be in no way party political, although in another sense our very existence will be political: we will be there to provide and demonstrate alternatives. We are likely to participate in local or national politics only if and insofar as we feel it to be essential for the community's welfare, in which case we may cast votes en bloc or otherwise take joint action. We are unlikely to stand in the way of political action by individuals.

Immigration

203

Everyone of us who is not a citizen of the country in which we locate the community will need to meet the requirements of that country's immigration laws. This crucial (but superable) matter will be covered in detail when we come to discuss the siting of Genesis (see p9).

□

Irrevocable commitment to any religion is not only intellectual suicide: it is positive unfaith because it closes the mind to any new vision of the world. Faith is, above all, openness — an act of trust in the unknown.

Alan Watts

There is only one person in charge of your universe. Some rationalizations offer God as an excuse for being irresponsible. They say that God is really in charge, not 'little old helpless me'.
You will have little difficulty with this. If God is in charge of the universe, He or She has certainly placed you as a working superintendent of the you-centred universe with which you deal and is not likely to excuse you from your job.

Harvey Jackins

Extracts from the Genesis Proposal

PERSONAL PROPERTY

247   The entire community structure — land, buildings and facilities — will belong to the community, with members' financial investments in the community being safeguarded and recoverable under the terms of our financial agreements (see p18).

248   Most other property will also be held in common by the members of the community. The terms on which personal possessions may be brought into and held in the community will be described in the property section of our Bylaws, which may be of more interest to incoming members than to anyone else. Essentially these terms will be that items which a member wishes *not* to share, or wishes to share with discretion, and which are small enough to be kept in a member's living-space may be retained as personal property. Almost everything else will either be shared fully with the community or not be brought into the community at all.

249   For example, books that a member feels relaxed about will go to form our library, and may be recovered by that member if ever co leaves the community. Cos surplus clothes will probably end up in the clothes store, freshly laundered and mended for anyone else to use for as long as they wish. A member's guitar will almost certainly live in cos bedroom; cos horse will be ridden by many of us and will come under the responsibility of the farm focalizer (see p21); and cos grand piano will probably have been sold or left behind when co entered   ☐
the community, because we already have two perfectly good ones.

PRIVACY

250   Members' rooms will be treated as inviolable and will provide as much privacy for their occupants as is wanted at any time. We will also treat with great respect the 'personal space' of others, 'personal space' being something which people will be able to carry around with them.   ☐

"Many of our visitors suppose that a community means a sacrifice of privacy. On the contrary, we've carefully provided for much more personal privacy than is likely to be found in the world at large. You may be alone here whenever you wish."   Walden Two

Extracts from the Genesis Proposal

PETS/WORKING ANIMALS

41

265 We will be riding horses, working with horses and probably talking with horses, and unless we decide otherwise we will have working relationshi~ ~ with donkeys, cows, goats and chickens. We are likely to co-operate with bees for part of their hon~ and with sheep for part of their wool. We will have a limited number of dogs and cats living with us: far f...wer than many of us would *like* to have around.

266 I hope that we and our children will have as many other opportunities as possible for relating to wildlife and to the animals who will be sharing our lives. Our aviary will be the sky and the trees, and our aquarium will be the rivers and lakes and sea: but *at the same time* we shall be harnessing species of the animal kingdom with the same awareness with which we shall be harnessing other aspects of nature and of ourselves.

□

If a child lives with criticism
  Co learns to condemn

If a child lives with hostility
  Co learns to fight

If a child lives with ridicule
  Co learns to be shy

If a child lives with shame
  Co learns to feel guilt

If a child lives with tolerance
  Co learns to be patient

If a child lives with encouragement
  Co learns confidence

If a child lives with praise
  Co learns to appreciate

If a child lives with fairness
  Co learns justice

If a child lives with security
  Co learns to have faith

If a child lives with approval
  Co learns to like coself

If a child lives with acceptance and friendship
  Co learns to find love in the world

I believe that this is what we have all been waiting for, that this is that final 'magic' moment in human history when we finally become what we are to become. Some may call it a revolution. But I believe revolution is really the wrong word for it, because what is happening today has never happened before and will never happen again.

We will finally catch sight of a vision of our true potential. We will see that we are the most important determinant of our own future and that we can become whatever we choose to become. We will see that the vast energies of our universe are available for our use, to create for ourselves an eternal existence of limitless freedom. 'We are as gods and might as well get good at it.'

Walter Szykitka, Public Works

Place the six days of creation in Genesis against the four billion years or so of the Earth's age. That is a ratio of 8,000 years to one second. All day Monday and up to Tuesday noon is the sheer formation of matter until there is a globe with oceans on it and mountains. Then a cell begins to undergo mitosis, dividing in two, and life is aboard the planet by Tuesday noon. All the rest of Tuesday and Wednesday, Thursday and Friday and well into Saturday, life expands and becomes more diverse, more stable, more beautiful. At four o'clock on the afternoon of Saturday, the last day of creation, the age of reptiles comes on-stage; at nine o'clock it goes off-stage. Just before the age of reptiles ends, there are redwoods — and just before redwoods, the pelican, a 90-million-year-old life form now threatened with extinction by DDT and man's urge to usurp the Earth. At three minutes before midnight, man appears. One quarter of a second before midnight, a bearded man, anti-establishment, talking of peace and brotherhood and Christianity is on the planet.

Then, one-fortieth of a second before midnight, enters the industrial revolution. You have heard it predicted that we can go on at this rate that has worked so splendidly for one-fortieth of a second because 'technology knows all the answers'. I am urging that we worry just a little bit about how much we know.

David R Brower

TOMORROW IS BUILT TODAY

leaders of the Emissaries of Divine Light. This meeting would have profound consequences for the future of the Genesis project. During the months following Rawlings return to the group on Iona further links were made with the Emissaries family in England and Genesis members attended a number of meetings and a weeklong 'Art of Living' seminar at Findhorn specially organised by the Emissaries for the Genesis group and 23 of the Findhorn focalisers. As their stay in the hotel on Iona came to an end in the spring the group made plans to move to Woking in Surrey to help out at The Ockenden Venture, a charity set up to help post-war displaced persons and now helping Vietnamese refugees. Who were planning an International Youth Festival of Hope for Mankind at which they hoped to get Buckminster Fuller and Mother Teresa to speak. Seemingly gone were the grand plans outlined in the Genesis prospectus.

"This step seems a far cry from our original 'vision' of Genesis as a worldwide network of communities, centres and linked individuals, for which the starting point would be a very large and beautiful house somewhere in Britain. That may or may not be so. We rejoice in our increasing willingness to flow in the current of the spirit, releasing whatever images we may have had. We are happy to let the picture for Genesis unfold as it will. We have been very blessed all the way."

Genesis Open Letter 4 March 1977

Chris Coates is the current Chair of the International Communal Studies Association and has documented the history of communal living in Britain in his two books Utopia Britannica *and* Communes Britannica.

A few Genesis members seem to have gone on to join the Emissaries, others drifted away from communal living. Copies of the *Genesis Proposal* continued to circulate around members of the alternative society or gathered dust on the bookshelves of one of the "thousand carefully selected individuals and organisations". Meanwhile the project itself slipped away into communal folklore.

Christiania Dreaming

HELEN JARVIS

And now for something completely different!
Christiania has become an almost mythical land.
It still deals in dreams but now also does
deals with the Danish state.

"It is one of those places I've heard about since I don't know when...the famous 'Freetown' Christiania with its notorious Pusher Street. How much is real and how much legend I can't tell- but there it is, on the map, in the heart of the Danish capital. How can such a large unruly population build homes, raise families and make decisions collectively- against the grain of state laws and social conventions? One day, I must go to Christiania and see for myself."

Helen's diary, 1990

The impulse I harboured years ago to 'see for myself' Europe's most enduring experiment in communal living is evidently shared by many hundreds of thousands of visitors who make Christiania the second most popular tourist destination in Copenhagen. Christiania features so frequently in tourist guides and handbooks on communal living- from faded photographs of naked camping, to quirky self-built homes and crowds of people, young and old, just hanging out in 'loser's paradise' – that first impressions can feel strangely familiar. But this post-card familiarity obscures the complex reality of an inhabited community that also serves a worldwide web of people who wistfully dream of a place they may never get to see for themselves.

Christiania exerts an extraordinarily intense and far-reaching influence, beyond its physical site, as an idea of freedom that captures the imagination. This is the first of many layers of contradictory meaning that I contemplate while walking from the Christianshavn Metro Station to Prinsessegade, to the entrance to Christiania and the traffic-free wild frontiers beyond. Appreciating what makes Christiania look and feel unique certainly offers a first layer of meaning and most people first learn about Christiania through a physical description of the place. There is that edgy prospect of novelty and provocation that evokes a heightened sense of being alive to new possibilities and ways of thinking differently about the future and the world. It's as if you're tripping on super-sensory stimulation- no chemicals required.

Notions of dreaming can be understood literally or metaphorically in the same way that some commentators insist on defining utopia in literal terms, as a fixed place or ideal state. Utopianism can be understood as a discursive strategy and as a method by which to unsettle static or derogatory stereotypes of romantic or nostalgic retreat from this world. In this sense, the impulse of thinking differently in and about Christiania travels the world in a transcendental flow of dreaming and enchantment; as a connected community of inspiration and learning. This helps to explain why so many non-visitors and casual visitors, without any legitimate means to live there, are deeply affected by it and sometimes identify with a sense of elective belonging to this as a spiritual home.

Just as Christiania attracts huge numbers of international tourists as the best known 'brand' to promote Denmark's progressive and liberated urban way of life, it also consciously flouts any semblance of formal planning and architectural norms of 'good' design. It is extraordinary in so many respects, not least the quirky assorted dwellings, some at remarkably low density, which give the appearance of this commune inhabiting a public art installation. It is a very open, public space. The fact that a lot of day-trippers come here and enjoy the place has always been hugely important in negotiations with the state, as evidence of continuing curiosity and relevance as a social experiment.

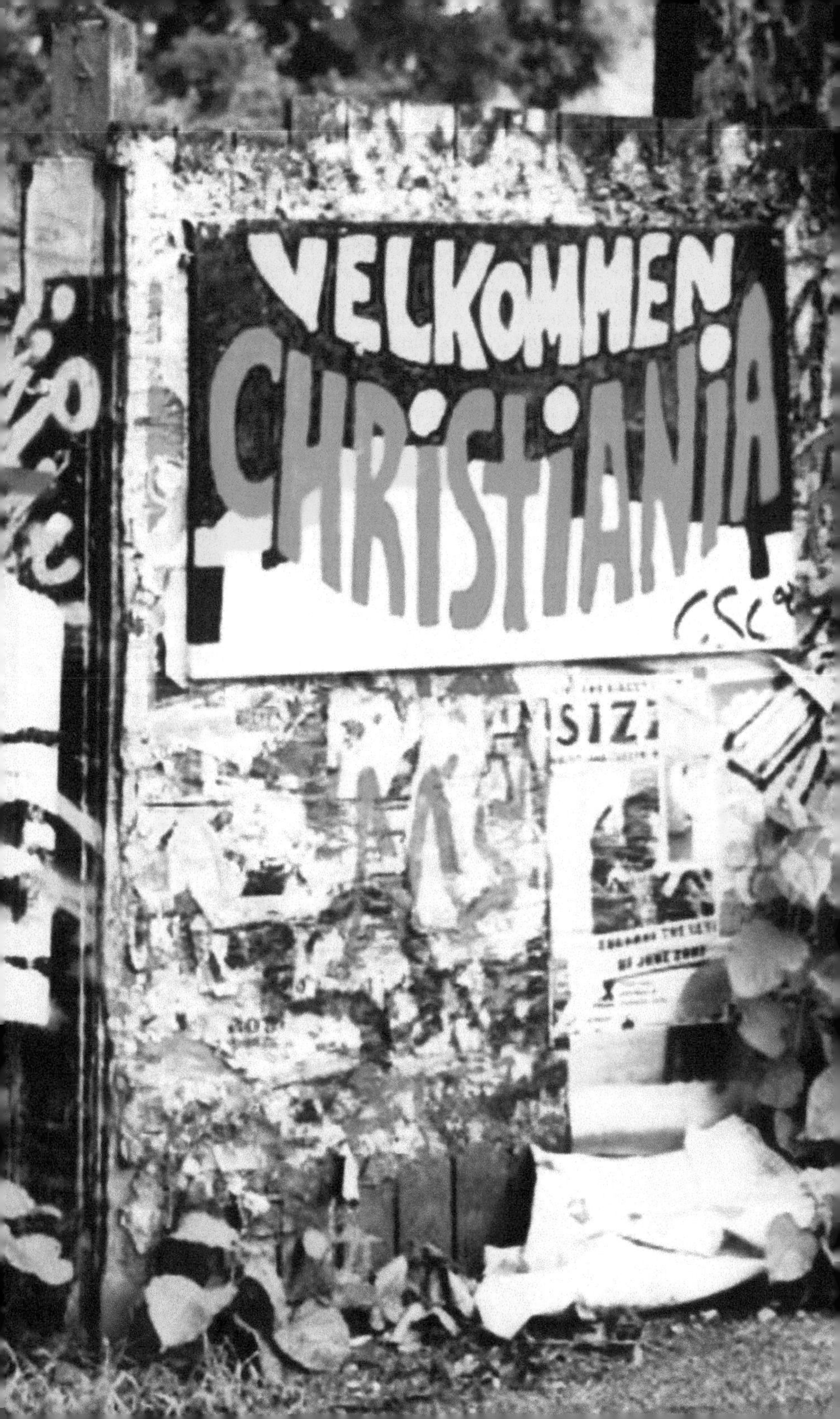
VELKOMMEN
CHRISTIANIA

The defining claim is that there is no private land in Christiania: it is all public and open to everybody. It is certainly an odd experience, walking or cycling through what appears to be someone's garden, surrounding a tiny house which looks to be scattered like a seed blown into the undergrowth. This historic openness now appears under threat and there are tell-tale signs in locked doors, fences and privacy notices that some residents feel overly exposed. The footpaths and trails for joggers and cyclists run tight by homes which by their DIY structures appear flimsy and vulnerable. Having tourists peer into your home can feel like you are living in a goldfish bowl or theme park.

Recording a classic of communal living

The story of how Christiania came into being has assumed legendary status in counter-cultural circles. According to the official 'Christiania Guide' (available to download free in English and Danish from the Christiania website):

The tale starts in 1969/70, when the fence at the corner of Prinsessegade and Refshalevej in the quarter of Copenhagen called Christianshavn is knocked down

several times by a group of local people to gain access to the large former military area within. Initially this infringement provides a playground for the local children but once the people of Christianshavn get their playground, the site attracts homeless squatters. Around this time, the alternative newspaper Hovedbladet (Head magazine) is published with the headline: 'emigrate with bus number 8'. The article tells about the abandoned military installations at Badmandsstræde Barracks, and includes lots of ideas for the use of the area- not least to house the great number of young people who cannot find anywhere to live. The result is the influx of people who want to create another life based on communal living and freedom, and thus Christiania is born – on the 26th September 1971 (Christiania Guide 2006: 3).

Versions of this story have been told at festivals and at political rallies over the intervening years and the headline trends have been published in national media and tourist magazines. This origin story has evolved through re-interpretation and the reality that there are many competing 'truths' about Christiania. Missing from the 'official' legacy, for instance, is the key role of Jacob Ludvigsen the young editor of *Hovedbladet* who coined the 'emigrate with bus 8' slogan, named the 'freetown' Christiania and co-authored Christiania's original manifesto. Ludvigsen faded from the story after he abandoned the site in 1972, disillusioned by the absence of order in common meetings. He is widely reported to have said that 'to live outside the law you must be honest'. This paraphrased line from a Bob Dylan song criticised the observed lawlessness among self-interested criminal groups. This song-line and the 'emigrated with bus 8' slogan frequently crop up in the networks and flows of utopian dreaming that communicate wistful yearning to transmit the spirit of Christiania to other sites and societies elsewhere.

The guided tour

Walking through the main entrance on Prinsessegade, the first-time visitor will notice a boldly inscribed overhead wooden sign that claims "You are now leaving the European Union". This marks the start of their journey into a liminal 'betwixt and between' place that defies conventional census categories: the built environment is neither planned by experts nor entirely unplanned; the landscape is neither urban nor rural – it is not in any sense agricultural, as might otherwise be expected of such a green oasis; the world-famous Christiania 'brand' makes money for the common purse, and numerous entrepreneurial creative industries thrive here, but in a local economy that is consciously stripped of commercial logos and the trappings of global capital. As a Freetown, Christiania has its own flag (three yellow dots on a red background) and, since 1997, its own local currency. The custom-made Løn coin can be used in 50 or so shops, eating places, music venues and businesses – ranging from bicycle repairs to recycled ovens – that spring up in the most unlikely corners of this public space.

While this counter-cultural settlement boasts many recognised features of Denmark's paradigmatic model of progressive and convivial public life, including traffic-free green landscape, its 'junkyard' aesthetic of unexpected magical encounters defies any blue-print that planners or policy makers would regard relevant to learn from. The Danish landscape architect Carl Theodor Sørenson coined the term 'Junk Playground' in 1931 in recognition of what he saw, from children playing on building sites and wasteland, as the creative benefits children gained from having autonomy to dream up their own place in the world. The vision of Christiania as an autonomous space for those excluded from the mainstream (whether by income or life-choice) echoes a similar appreciation.

From the outset the unspoken rule was that buildings were to be adapted rather than torn down and this shaped the aesthetic that exists today. When the Bådsmandsstræde Barracks site was first occupied there were approximately 150 existing buildings, including the rare, half-timbered, Commanders House (Fredens Ark), 17th and 18th century powder magazines on the bastians, a large indoor riding arena (Den grå hal) and a smaller riding house (Den grønne hal). These historic buildings, which now have conservation status with the National Heritage Agency, were unused and very run-down when squatters took up residence in 1971. The following years saw the original buildings incrementally modified and upgraded and approximately 175 new buildings added. By 1975, the resident population was 850-900, similar to what it is today. From its early days, do-it-yourself home construction, renovation and maintenance reflected two potentially colliding extremes of Danish society. On the one hand

CHRISTIANIAS NYE GRUNDLOV
CHRISTIANIA'S NEW COMMON LAW

CHRISTIANIAS MÅLSÆTNING ER AT OPBYGGE ET SELVSTYRENDE
SAMFUND, HVOR HVERT ENKELT INDIVID FRIT KAN UDFOLDE SIG
UNDER ANSVAR OVERFOR FÆLLESSKABET.

CHRISTIANIA'S COMMITMENT IS TO CREATE AND SUSTAIN A
SELF-GOVERNING COMMUNITY, IN WHICH EVERYONE IS FREE TO
DEVELOP AND EXPRESS THEMSELVES AS RESPONSIBLE MEMBERS
OF THE COMMUNITY.

ELSK HINANDEN
LOVE EACH OTHER

SPIL MUSIK
PLAY MUSIC

KYS
KISS

BØVS
BURP

FODRE DIN SKILDPADDE
FEED YOUR TURTLE

FÅ BØRN
HAVE BABIES

PLUK BLOMSTER
PICK FLOWERS

GÅ PÅ TOILETTET
GO TO THE TOILET

LAV LEJRBÅL
HAVE A BONFIRE

was an experimental, constantly evolving, entrepreneurial quest for freedom – flere fristeder (more free space): a retreat from authority, individualism, private ownership and mass market merchandise. On the other hand was a yearning for authentic being-and-belonging – hygge: broadly translated as simple, natural and 'cosy'. In mainstream society, hygge is typically manifest in a café culture of shared snacks and a home décor involving the selection and display of boutique candles. Beyond this 'look', the intention is to evoke a timeless release from hypermodernity. In Christiania, this intention is interpreted ideologically, as a project of moral, ecological achievement; making a home, literally, from salvaged materials and time-honoured craft skills. Self-build is a way of reclaiming from 'experts' and 'commerce' the intimate significance of habitation. Whereas the junkyard playground ethos is best interpreted as the absence of order, there is parallel evidence of exquisite care and craft skill – where qualities of hygge are celebrated in the local culture of home-making. Christiania flouts not only urban policies but also social and material conventions.

Over time Christiania has come to be organised into 14 discrete areas. While the casual observer is unlikely to differentiate between the local identities of each, the intimidating local reputation of Pusher Street is an exception: it occupies a tiny fraction of this 85 acre site and yet it is the one discrete area that visitors never fail to identify. At the same time they will struggle to navigate the looping footpaths and eclectic jumble of characterful buildings, many of them blending in with the untamed natural landscape. The disorienting absence of street lighting and road signs leads many to rely on a resident guide to help them locate famous architectural curiosities such as the Bananhuset (Banana House), the Glass House, the Pagoda and a tiny house resembling a recently landed UFO that is nestled among the reeds at the water's edge of the lake. Without a local guide, following directions to a particular landmark is like reciting a fairy-tale riddle: "turn right at the willow thicket, up by the rope swing, look for a pirate ship and there you'll find the hot potato". For the 850 or so adults and children who inhabit Christiania and the smaller proportion who undertake community jobs (e.g. bakery, gardening, laundry, machine hall) for which they are allocated a common wage, the way that the Common Purse and collective aspects of the Freetown are mediated through discrete local areas is highly significant.

Dealing in dreams and doing deals with the state

Christiania continued to operate outside the legal framework for 40 years until February 2011 when the Danish state proposed a 'take it or leave it' deal in which residents were obliged to buy the land and original buildings that they had illegally occupied. For a community fiercely opposed to the idea of private property and ownership this was a fraught decision. Ultimately the deal was accepted by claims that to purchase the land as a collective Christiania would be protected from any individual or corporate entity being able to control or sell it in the future. The idea was for Christiania to 'buy itself free of speculation' as a common resource for 'everybody and nobody'. This way Christiania could remain largely intact, even as it was forced to accept the same planning regulations and building controls as for the rest of Danish society. While this brought to a close a legendary tale of struggles with all manner of state authorities, new conflicts have emerged between pusher enclaves and artist and activist areas.

● ● ● ● ● ● ● ● ● ● ●

66

The idea was for Christiania to buy itself free of speculation

99

● ● ● ● ● ● ● ● ● ● ●

On 1st July 2012 the Christiania Foundation was created to purchase the land and buildings for 125 million Danish kroner (16.8 million euros). Deductions were made to compensate for the renovation and maintenance of the water, sewers, electricity, rights of ways and the rural open spaces that Christianites agreed to undertake. Of the final sum of 52 million kroner, 46 million kroner came from a collective mortgage and 6 million kroner came from the sale of the so-called 'Peoples Christiania Share' (Folkeaktie). It was the conscious intention that this crowd-funding source of donations (the shares are symbolic and have no economic value) would reach out to the many hundreds of thousands of people around the world who hold cherished memories and dreams of Christiania. In the first 30 months this emotional connection raised 11.2 million kroner representing one seventh of the 76 million kroner sum required.

It remains a moot point whether the deal that was struck was favourable to all or some Christianites and if it preserved or betrayed the original idea and spirit of the 'Christiania way'. Before accepting the deal, the community closed its public entrances to engage in 4 days of profound soul-searching (from 27th to 30th April 2011). Whether or not the closure was symbolic, to demonstrate what Copenhagen would lose if Christiania were to become a private 'gated community', or whether it afforded time and peace in which to contemplate the latest state ultimatum, opinion remained deeply divided. Notwithstanding its radically democratic form of consensus decision-making, Christiania is shot through with unresolved conflict. For example, a small minority of residents argued vociferously for normalization to make it possible for individuals to buy their own homes. Others expressed Christiania's frustration with the state's ultimatum through an interpretive dance.

Enchantment

It is one thing to visit Christiania and to witness and challenge first-hand the stories that circulate about this place. It is quite another to gain an insider perspective. I am fortunate to have lived here for a short time in 2010 and again in 2011 during the extraordinary celebrations for Christiania's 40th birthday, hosted by the Christiania Researcher in Residence (CRIR)

initiative. I lived for several weeks with my daughter in the cosy CRIR house (a small wagon built into the side of the lakeside ramparts) in the Mælkebøtten (Dandelion) area. Being embedded in the rhythm of the place encouraged deeper reflection and more enduring relationships to form (mothering alongside other mothers) than would be possible as a complete outsider. We attended public festivals, such as Christiania's 'alternative' Grundlovsdag (Constitution Day), as well as a more intimate community fund-raising event at the Operaen. It felt natural to assume the slow pace and parochial scale in our daily routines: cycling the length and breadth of the site; shopping for groceries at the Indkøbscentralen and Grønsagen; frequenting the community cafes and eating-places – getting to know people and getting ourselves known. From living as a resident I reacted with thinly veiled horror whenever anyone claimed to know and represent the place from a fleeting experience. From living as a resident I could appreciate multiple, ambivalent, liminal qualities to the social organisation and cultural identity that would prevent me ever claiming to know it.

> 66
> *Christiania's history is a long and tangled tale of struggles, not only with the Danish state but also with property developers who circle this prime real estate like sharks*
> 99

The CRIR initiative encouraged me to look beyond any fixed site or visible landmark for Christiania's place in the world of travelling ideas and inspiration. Belief that Christiania is relevant and important as a field of interest beyond the site it occupies galvanized a group of Christianites, ex-Christianites and associated scholars to launch the Christiania Researcher in Residence (CRIR) programme in 2004. They were motivated by an understanding that Christiania's future depended on support and understanding both from other Danes and from outside of Denmark. Christiania's history is a long and tangled tale of struggles, not only with the Danish state but also with property developers who circle this prime real estate like sharks. It also reflects years of active and creative cultural production and efforts to 'reach out' and engage with the wider world. CRIR is one of many hubs of activity such as the culture group of Kulturforening which organizes regular exchange visits and conferences with the cultural quarter of Ruigoord in Amsterdam, the idea being to develop and expand Christiania values around the world. A similar impulse prompted squatter activists living in AKC Metelkova, an autonomous social centre in the middle of Ljubljana, Slovenia, to undertake a similar cultural exchange. AKC Metelkova shares many similarities with Christiania because it too is an occupied site of former military barracks. Similarly, artists representing the Gängeviertel (12 occupied houses of Hamburg) were motivated by a shared experience of informal urbanism to learn more about Christiania buy living in the CRIR house while curating an exhibition on squatting in the art gallery (Galloperiet) in 2013.

Networks and flows of dreaming, enchantment and critical utopian thinking

By recognising the networks and flows of dreaming and enchantment connections are made between the imagined, enacted 'inspiration' of Christiania and the experience and enchantment of living there or witnessing first-hand what this might be like. This approach begins to reclaim a dynamic process from the static notion of utopia more frequently used as a pejorative term of naïve idealism. It considers the function of utopian dreaming as a way of unsettling and challenging the dominant culture of the day, uncovering processes that are already entailed in experimentation. Existential quests coexist with a narrower utopia in political discourse. By emphasising a utopian method of thinking about resistance and yearning, a more nuanced and situated understanding of what it entails to live together in community emerges. It shows how these experiences can change the world in ordinary, unknown and unexpected ways.

Crucially, understanding Christiania's place in the world is complicated by multiple spheres of influence. On the one hand, Christiania is peculiarly rooted in the messy, fleshy territory of 'living together' in a way that activist social movements are not. Living for a while in the CRIR house I experienced profound reluctance to step out of this bubble existence. On the other hand, the 'Christiania effect' can be described in magical terms, as an embodied and enacted spirit that transcends a territorial place. It can arouse a sense of enchantment that many visitors hold and carry with them into subsequent encounters. This evokes the transformational impact attributed to intentional communities and autonomous societies elsewhere. In the UK, for instance, feminist activists who lived for a time at the anti-nuclear peace camp of Greenham Common in the 1980s reported that they 'carried the spirit of Greenham home' such that shared experience of collective action permanently altered the way they viewed the world.

Helen Jarvis is Reader in Social Geography at Newcastle University. Her interest include collaborative housing, intentional communities and communal studies, cohousing, self-directed cities, informal urbanism and community-led development.

The concept of 'hygge' has been used to draw attention to the mutuality, conviviality and tolerance that make Christiania 'difficult to leave' and 'a good life to live' for parents with young children in particular. There is evidence that this mode of living shields Christiania from the hectic pace and brashness of the outside world, emphasising instead an intimate scale of shared space and collective care. The question remains; what lessons are there here for planners and environmentalists wishing to cultivate mutuality and conservation in mainstream urban public space? How is it that Christiania can provide a place for people to make their own home, where Copenhagen pointedly does not; those people who do not 'fit' or whose unpaid caring work goes unrewarded? Asking these questions does highlight the need to unravel processes of utopian thinking from opposing forces of unintended conflict – notably between pushers, artists and activists, each enacting their own version of the Christiania dream.

Let's talk about Power

ROGER HALLAM

*What happens when you fail to find the happy medium between
the tyranny of structurelessness and the bureaucracy of anarchy?
Roger highlights how assets can all too easily slip out of
co-operative control.*

I no longer live in a co-op. A few years ago, after dedicating a good twenty years to the co-op cause, I found myself sitting in a room, not allowed to speak, and having the membership of my co-op removed. I found out about the other two co-op members intentions – not through them but – from a solicitor's letter which arrived one day out of the blue. A few weeks later I received another letter saying that the land I had farmed organically for the past 12 years was being sold and my lease would not be renewed. For the next four years I did not know if I was to be evicted and had no power to influence that decision. I felt like a peasant under the thumb of his feudal landlord. It was not good.

The point of this article however is not to indulge in complaining about a rather unpleasant period of my life but rather to look critically – and ultimately hopefully – at the dark side of the world of co-ops and communities. After all isn't that what us radicals are supposed to do by definition – get to the roots of things. And the root of things, in this case, I want to argue is the tricky issue of power.

People set up co-ops and communities for a number of reasons but it's a fair bet that a big part of the motivation is to get control over their lives. "Taking Control" was the slogan of Radical Routes with which I was closely involved for the first 15 years of its existence.

We do not want to be humiliated, ordered around, and be made insecure by the power of landlords and bosses. Sounds good. But there is a problem. Power – the ability to make other people do things – does not disappear the day you register your co-op. As long as there are decisions to be made and access to collective resources to be decided on then power very much still exists. The issue then is not about getting rid of power but of making it equal and accountable. We make decisions together and encourage each other to participate. Issues are decided on in the open and written down.

Making sure that people are equal and accountable

The question, however, remains who is going to make sure these things happen? In Radical Routes (RR), as a national organisation of radical housing co-ops and worker co-ops, there were rules and expectations created to ensure that power was made equal and distributed. Roles were rotated, co-ops expected to participate in decision making and given equal access to these processes. It all seemed good but there was a critical flaw in the design of this rule made to equalise power. This was in the relationship between individual member co-ops and Radical Routes as a national organisation. As many readers may know Radical Routes was – and still is – in the business of helping people set up co-ops and loaning them money to buy houses or set up social enterprises. However, once the loan is given RR has no control over the conduct of the primary co-ops. So the question is who ensures that the power in these co-ops remain equal and accountable?

And in many cases this power, with its potential for abuse, increases over time. Property values can rise dramatically and mortgages are paid off. In the case of my co-op, the farm we bought cost £190,000 but twelve years later its value had risen to £700,000. Also over time the original radically committed members often leave. There is an increasing incentive to limit membership to a few – often two or three people – so they don't need to share out the increasing goodies. Lastly power is increased, paradoxically, by a radical culture that can demand more from people than just their rent for being member-tenants. They need to be doing radical and communal things and if they are not there is the ability to deny them their fundamental liberal rights. People can be denied permanent membership rights because they are not radical enough – not "psychologically" suitable – not our type of people. And who decides this? Of course it's the existing members – they are both judge and jury. So there is a lot of power to be had and as the phrase goes, power corrupts, and absolute power corrupts absolutely.

My argument then is that by setting up independent "radical" co-ops you are setting yourself up for a major fall. The situation I found myself in is not a one-off but a systematic problem which has come to be called "carpet-bagging" in the movement. The typical situation is two people close down a co-op to new members and effectively privatise the co-op's assets as their own property which they carry round with them. And in this grab for money and power things happen to people like me which are the opposite of everything that co-ops were set up to do. This is not just about money but interpersonal abuse and bullying. Outrageous behaviour in co-ops and communities – which make big claims on their members' lives – too often results in this abuse because the abusers are unaccountable to anyone outside to what are essentially scarily closed worlds. This dark side of co-ops and communities has been endemic since the modern movement got going in the early 1970s. Everyone involved in this movement knows of numerous examples of horrendous situations of power abuse and the embarrassing degeneration of places which were supposed to be example of alternative idealism. I spent a good few years as a facilitator and mediator trying to pull various groups back from the absyss – in all cases they were autonomous and no one from the outside could call time on the abuse that was going on. I remember one community, set up in the heyday of communes in the 1970s, which was effectively controlled by one guy who no longer lived on site. It was obviously a ridulous situation but no other communities or co-ops wanted to get seriously involved. There were some half-hearted attempts at mediation which I was asked to organise but the intervention was basically pathetic. This was not because a lot of individuals were not very concerned but because of

> **66** *people close down a co-op to new members and effectively privatise the co-op's assets as their own property* **99**

collective action. People want to see a collective good come about but no one wants to make the first move. This is what structurelessness creates – tyranny – as is the title of the famous booklet on the subject[7].

More often than not in these situations the law gets involved and the idea of living outside the system leads to the exact opposite. Being taken over by the system's most authoritarian aspects in the form of the police and the courts. Again this situation is endemic – it's not about bad apples or "interesting" personalities although they certainly don't help. It happens too often for that to be the case. And it is still happening at the moment – places where people are treated in appalling ways which would never happen in a conventional liberal framework. When alternative things go bad we cannot avoid the fact they go really bad.

Do we stay in denial?

So much for the bad news. The question is: do we stay in denial about this dark side of our movement? Do we pretend – as the Catholic Church has done over child abuse – that they are individual cases, that the system is sound? Or do we have the courage and true radicalness to bring this problem into the light and see it for what it is? A mess! And do we have courage to reassess some of our fundamental prejudices and ideological blindness, which I argue are at the heart of this problem which we continually recreate?

Let's be clear then the problem is unaccountable power. Power is always present and no amount of idealistic wishful thinking is going to get it to go away. Like the washing up in a student house, if no one deals with it, it will still be there in the morning! And you can structure it so that everyone does their share – or deny there is a problem or a structure is needed which means one or two people end up doing it. And this is the rub. Without structure you get abuse and exploitation. Structure, properly designed, means accountability and fairness. What was closed and hidden, is opened up and challengeable. Necessarily – and this is the crucial issue – it requires a giving up of total autonomy and freedom. You can't get out of the washing up because "you don't want to do it right now" – you are on the rota, tough!

And so let's take the situation with RR and by implication all the other situations where co-ops are set up with no accountability to the wider movement. The key problem is that the member co-ops are ultimately independent. At the end of the day they can leave the organisation whatever RR says about them engaging in abuse and/or carpet-bagging. The fundamental solution to this is that that all RR's co-op should be ultimately and legally under the control of RR itself. This would mean two things. If there was a case of serious abuse the issue could go to binding arbitration. Each side would give its case, the evidence would be considered, and the result would be final and enforceable. This could be done in a democratic and transparent way. Instead of tales of abuse going on for years it could be effectively challenged and stopped. Similarly a rump of members could not carpet-bag a co-op. RR could enforce an open membership policy. It simply would not be possible to run off with the assets because they would belong to RR rather than the members.

Of course all this needs to be designed in a balanced and sensitive way. There could and should be ongoing processes of accountability so most problems are identified and nipped in the bud. There should be ongoing and ideally compulsory training in how to run a co-op and how basic co-op principles should be enacted. Then if and when problems arise there should be the provision of facilitation and mediation to try to sort the problem out. But last of all – and of vital importance – there can be binding arbitration as outlined above. With this structure then it is clear that a co-op would still be effectively autonomous in the way that we all agree it should be. We don't need to be raising false alarms or ideological objections about the centre/hierarchy controlling the grassroots etc. What we are saying is simply that co-ops should not have the kind of autonomy which would permit abuse and carpet-bagging.

> " *co-ops should not have the kind of autonomy which would permit abuse and carpet-bagging* "

In a nutshell then, if you get evicted from your home and from your co-op for no good reason, being offered mediation is at best irrelevant and at worst an insult. What you want is justice. This is what we say when we campaign for a more just society – regulation of

companies and banks – and so it should be when we deal with our own internal affairs. Anything else is frankly hypocrisy. We often hear in the media the great excuse for when things go wrong in society's institutions – that it's because of a few bad apples. That there is no need for reform or accountability, we just need to root out the bad people and the system can stay the same. You hear that too often in the alternative movement as well – gossip about bad people – how things have gone wrong because of Person X. Often of course this is part of the story but it is a fundamentally conservative orientation. The fact of the matter (and any radical analysis would support it) is that situations create bad people not the other way round. If there is unaccountable power to be had, it will be obtained and used for abuse. The key issue then is to make that power accountable.

In my research on participatory structures this issue is always a key design challenge. In every successful case of real world effective participation and co-operation there is always a two way control structure. The parts control the centre and the centre controls the parts – there is a binding together of accountability. For instance, in probably the most successful participatory governance system in the world, in Porto Alegri in Brazil, general assemblies in city neighbourhoods decide on budget priorities for the city. They then send delegates to an open and transparent committee which collates the proposals and creates the priorities. This is what we would all expect and applaud. But what is less noticed and equally important is that the structure and organisation of the neighbourhood assemblies is overseen by the city council to ensure against abuse, corruption, and other bad practice. It is not possible for these assemblies to be taken over by sectional interests or criminal elements. Since this process was fully institutionalised in the 1990s there has been a massive fall in corruption and a transformational increase in the provision of local services and infrastructures. Of course like any real world process it has many flaws but it is an inspiring example of what can be achieved by good participatory design.

And this is the positive side of this issue. Once we have got over our aversion to accountable structures and ideological dogmatism about total autonomy, we can see how this design creates confidence and growth rather than embarrassment and disillusionment. As I have written in my booklet *Anarchist Economics* the key to fulfilling our dream of a sustained and large scale alternative/co-operative sector in this capitalist society is for the resources of the parts to be collectively controlled and used to create further growth. The other side of stopping carpet-bagging is that the assets created by the paying off of mortages can be used by the centre to help fund and lever more loans for new co-operative projects. This is the key mechanism which allowed the massive growth of the Co-operative Movement in Britain in the nineteenth and early twentieth century and the Mondragon Co-operatives in Spain in the 1950's. The prospect then is that the asset of the co-ops, controlled by the whole organisation, are put to use where there is most need and most potential for growth. This is the basic principle of redistribution which, again, we are demanding of capitalist society. We should be applying this to ourselves. The assets of wealthy co-ops should be redistributed to new and poor co-ops. Again, this needs to be done in a structured, open and democratic way. But this is more than possible with a bit of good design.

Of course, as ever, there is a problem with legal structures here. We can hopefully all agree this is the way to

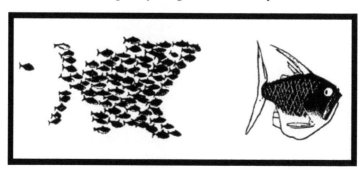

go but we need to find a way in which RR and/or any new organisation can have ultimate legal control of the assets of its member co-ops. This is not an insurmountable problem and there are people already working on this challenge. It is worth remembering that it took a number of years for open, fully mutual housing co-ops to find a solid legal form. When, around 1990, I worked together with other unemployed activists to see how we could set up a co-op and get hold of a house, we benefited from the quiet but vital work of other co-op innovators who developed the primary rules we were then able to pick up and run with.

The big challenge now is to find a legal form for secondary co-operative development which a new generation of co-operative activists can take up and make fly. I would suggest that effective secondary development is the key task and the exciting prospect for the next decade. The major difference between now and the period when I was involved in setting up RR is that the situation now is much more promising but also more demanding. Back in the heyday of neo liberalism in the 1990s it seems co-ops could only ever be a side show in the world of exuberant free market capitalism. Serious co-operators were a tiny minority in a culture of extreme radical purism with its anti-structuralist addition to total autonomy – which ironically reflected the fetish of total freedom promoted by neo-liberalism. Since the 2008 financial crash, capitalism looks no longer shiny and new but is seen for the absurdity that it is. Millions of people are now open to a new way of organising society and we are guardians of the tradition which has the answers. This is a great opportunity but we also have a duty to get it right. The stakes have never been higher. So let's not keep messing it up and get those structures sorted.

Roger Hallam wrote an article for the first ever edition of D&D. As one of the founders of Radical Routes he's been on the front lines of co-operative living for more than a quarter-century. He is at present doing a PhD at Kings College, London in the design of participatory structure for radical political collective action. He is also an organic grower. Contact him on organics2go@ googlemail.com

- *This is a shortened version of a more animated account of the problems and opportunities for co-operation:* The Poverty of Post-scarcity Anarchism.

1 *Jo Freeman's booklet* The Tyranny of Structurelessness *was first published in various forms in the 1970s. A version of the text is accessible at www.jofreeman.com/joreen/tyranny.htm*

Buddying Up

ROBERT MORRIS

*For those of you who remember 'Fairground'
here is the modern day re-envisioning.
For those who don't... this proposed system could stop
money going in through the front door and out through the back.*

It's 7:50am on a Sunday morning. I'm standing on the platform waiting for a train to Hebden Bridge. It takes a lot for me to be out of bed at this hour on a weekend, but this is important. Radical Routes is holding a meeting to bring together its key legal and financial brains to look into if/how a brand new way of working could be adopted.

Walking up the hill from the station, I was trying to figure out which of the many stone buildings was hosting the meeting. As I rounded a bend, I came upon the sign "Nutclough Tavern".

I'd arrived at the venue of what will be known in the annals of housing co-op history as "the Hebden Bridge meeting". I had been invited in order to make a presentation, and here's how it began:

"My advice to Radical Routes – stop lending money to housing co-ops..."

You could have cut the silence with a knife. Everybody knew that Radical Routes needed more co-ops and thus far lending to them had been key, so why on earth would it stop?

Fast forward to the following year...

It's lovely spring day, the sun is shining and there's not a cloud in the sky. I'm working on a roof – I climbed out of a skylight window down a ladder (don't worry, I'm also being belayed on a rope, just in case) to repair a flashing.

One of the wonderful things about co-ops and communities is the combination of practical work (such as building maintenance or vegetable growing) and social occasions (like shared evening meals and having guests to stay) mixed in with some quite serious legal and financial stuff. And all done with the same people, in the same place. During your time spent in intentional communities you certainly have opportunities to develop in any of these areas, if you want to.

"So," you might ask, "if intentional communities are such a great thing, how come there isn't one on every street corner?"

Back on the roof, I've fixed the flashing, climbed back in, and been given a cup of tea by one of the residents.

The people who live in this house are all members of a legal entity called Cordata Housing Co-operative Ltd. They have a standard legal form, technically known as a "fully mutual housing co-operative", and were registered using a set of rules by Radical Routes dating from 1996, itself a rehashing of earlier rules.

But there the similarity with traditional housing co-ops ends. For one thing, the house that Cordata occupies is no ordinary house: it's a co-operative eco-house, refurbished with a full range of energy performance measures, before the members moved in. The idea is not only to allow the co-op members to reduce their environmental impact but also to give them a high-standard property to make community/co-op living an attractive idea for a greater range of people.

Traditionally, each fully mutual housing co-op has bought its own property, using rental income to pay the mortgage off. This has often resulted in rents going down over time (in real terms, at least), which hardly seems fair given that founders and members in the early years who put all the effort into getting the co-op set up are effectively subsidising the living costs of later members.

Another downside of this model is that the properties usually available for housing co-ops to buy are often not in a good state, and need to be improved. Without funding for refurbishment built in from day one, co-ops have had to do things piecemeal as and when permitted by finances and people's capacities.

With Cordata, however, the building was bought and refurbished by the Co-operative Living Freehold Society (CLFS), the first of a new breed of co-op organisation trying to put the new model into practice. This is the first house for CLFS, which I co-founded, and that is why I was up on that roof.

But getting the co-op off to a good start is only one benefit of this new model. In the past, co-op umbrella bodies such as Radical Routes have focused on the start-up of new co-ops at the expense of structures that could help imagine their future development. The result has been that older co-ops have collapsed or have wound down – for a variety of reasons.

By 2015, the net size of the housing co-op movement is considerably smaller than it might have been; it has remained relatively static over the years because the money is effectively going in the front door and out of the back door.

With the right legal and imaginative structures in place, with the money recycled in a different way, the housing co-op movement might now be bigger and more embedded in the public imagination. This is all the more important when demand for co-op living is higher than it has been for many years.

> **with the money recycled in a different way, the housing co-op movement might now be bigger and more embedded in the public imagination**

The difference between Cordata and other housing co-ops is more than just financial. Radical Routes co-ops were previously set up with founder members doing all the work of looking for properties, buying them and getting the finance together, often burning themselves out in the process.

With our approach, second-tier organisations, such as CLFS, help out with all that heavy lifting – plus eco-refit – significantly reducing the labour needed by the co-op members who might be new to housing co-ops and not have all the required skills. In exchange, once they are all settled into their new co-op, members are expected to share skills and do some work in creating other housing co-ops. This creates a new kind of chain reaction – something that was missing before.

Radical Routes tried to create a sustainable way of getting co-op members to contribute to the running of the organisation through "work commitment", where each co-op member has to complete a designated task as a condition of that co-op receiving a Radical Routes' loan.

The problem that emerged with this is that once the co-op has paid off its loan, it can leave Radical Routes and the work commitment stops. The CLFS-style approach is more sustainable because the second-tier organisation owns the property and the housing co-op can never "divorce" itself from the wider organisation.

In theory, the fully mutual principle – that the people who live in a co-op house, and only those people, are given full control of it – is preferable because it is the most empowering to the individuals concerned and minimises the influence of contrary interests.

But the experience of the past 20 years is that, in practice, things don't always work so well. Apart from a few cases of people deliberately mismanaging co-ops to actually or effectively take common ownership assets for personal gain, there are far more routine issues.

For example, the process of setting up and then running an intentional community housing co-op gets increasingly complex as time goes on, with many factors intervening, such as increasing legislation or an ever-tougher housing market. Generally speaking, people are having to spend more time in the process of obtaining the money they need, leaving less time to devote on an unpaid basis to the co-ops.

The result is that the ideal size for a group – in order for it to have all the right skills and the capacity to do all the necessary work – increases at a time when the days of large (20-30 or larger) "commune" style co-ops seem to be over due to the greater difficulty there now is in acquiring larger properties.

One solution that has been used is to put several houses together in a single co-op: for example, Sanford Housing Co-op in southeast London has 125 residents spread over 15 properties. The disadvantage here is such a large number of people results in lack of engagement.

With the two-tier model we're developing, most decisions – including membership and a lot of the day-to-day financial stuff – is handled at individual house level, with more strategic and specialised work being done at the second-tier level.

With all this in place, I'm quietly confident that the benefit of my roofing efforts will in their own small way benefit the housing co-op movement, rather than ending up in individual pockets.

Robert Morris
Founder member,
The Drive Housing
Co-op (2010
onwards).
Founder member,
Co-operative Living
Freehold Society
(2013 onwards).
Active participator
in housing co-op
development work
nationally through
Radical Routes legal
working group and
Friendly Housing
Action.

Meanwhile, back at the Hebden Bridge meeting...

Radical Routes has now taken on board this model and is looking to develop a variant of it where they buddy up a more mature housing co-op with a new group. This serves two purposes: the new group gets real hands-on help with its workload from the mature co-op; and in addition some of the equity in the mature co-op can be unlocked to assist the new co-op.

At the time of writing, Radical Routes is putting together a plan to make this happen, with a legal party fleshing out the details.

Where did it all start?

CHRIS COATES

A long term member of the editorial collective asks
where did the idea for Diggers and Dreamers come from?
And what has it got up to along the way?

Well you might say that it all began in 1989 over a pint or two at the The Old Thatched Inn at Adstock just north of Redfield community in Buckinghamshire after a long day's meeting discussing what to call the follow up to the *Communes Network Info Pack* – I'm not sure who said it should make some reference to Gerrard Winstanley and the 1649 Diggers colony, but we were soon off on a naming riff...The *Diggers Directory, 1649 and all that, From Digging to Communing, Where have all the Diggers gone?*... eventually leading to – *Diggers & Dreamers* – which like all good names still seemed to work for us all the following morning after we had slept on it.

Or perhaps you could say that it began back in 1983 with a small advert in the October issue of the *Communes Network* magazine inviting people interested in producing a video and information pack about communes to a meeting at Redfield. The idea was to produce a video and accompanying Information pack aimed at "schools and other groups who want to hire/borrow it" and that "might also be useful for people in the initial stages of setting up a community." It proved harder than anticipated to produce the video and after a number of meetings attended by members of several different communities the group decided to go ahead and produce the *Communes Network Information Pack* – as a "general introduction to the nitty-gritty and issues of communal living." The *Info Pack*, which was published in July 1985, consisted of a green folder with 14 communes fact sheets in it covering topics ranging from "Alternatives to the Nuclear Family" to "Earning a Living in a Community" and "Young People and Children in Communities". Plus a copy of the current *CN* magazine, a directory and a few samples of publicity sheets from individual communes.

Or then again maybe it really began way back on the 15th/16th of February 1975 with the demise of the Communes Movement and the birth of Communes Network at the Gorilla Family commune at Aston. About 30 people had gathered in Birmingham that weekend to decide what to do about the, by then, somewhat moribund Communes Movement that had had it's heyday in the late sixties and early seventies.

"...there was no protocol nor tradition to follow. Nobody could have foretold the outcome. But over the course of the weekend we evolved a leaderless consensus style and came to some harmonious decisions..."
CM Newsletter 104 14.3.75

The new Communes Network was to be different from the Communes Movement. It was to be more modest in its aims: supporting "the spread of communes generally" and no longer aspiring towards what was referred to as the 'grandiose Federal society based on the free commune' that had been the aim of the Communes Movement. The Network was to have 'no constitution' and decisions were to be taken by consensus. Very quickly the new communes' organisation produced its first newsletter, *Network* 1.

"The main aim of this Network is to bring us all closer together as friends. We're trying to get to know each other, so what we're after is not a mammoth effort, once and for all, a condensed, impersonal account of your grand plan: it's an ongoing account of what you're actually doing, newsletter by newsletter, just the bits you'd write in a short note to old friends – which is what it is."
Network 1, 14 March 1975

The aims of the Communes Network were set out as simply "to encourage the growth of communes and collectives" and to do this through a monthly newsletter, a Directory of Communes and other booklets on matters relating to collectives.

You could keep going back in time and saying it all began with this or that; with the publication of the *Communes Journal* in the late 1960's or even the pre-war *Community Broadsheet* and in truth all these publications are *Diggers & Dreamers* forerunners. But the actual trigger for the production of the first edition of *D&D* came from the members of a few communities who had stayed together as a group to oversee the sales and distribution of the *CN Info Pack*. The pack had sold well by mail-order throughout the second half of the 1980's, but bookshops hated it – because it was a folder with loose sheets that fell out in the shop and got dog-eared and tattered from people looking at them – so it was decided that the follow-up would be a proper book.

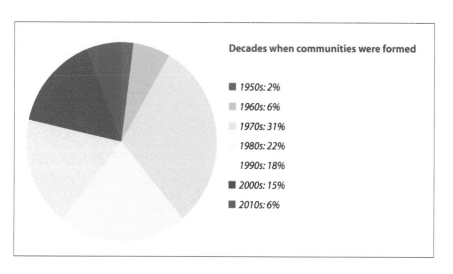

Decades when communities were formed

- 1950s: 2%
- 1960s: 6%
- 1970s: 31%
- 1980s: 22%
- 1990s: 18%
- 2000s: 15%
- 2010s: 6%

25 years of Digging & Dreaming

In the first edition of *Diggers & Dreamers* we declared its objectives were to "dispel the myth that – communes came and went with the 60's" and at the same time "bring the idea of communal living to the attention of more people." The driving motivation was to produce a journal and directory that presented a 'public face of communal living', that was easily available and accessible to a wide range of people. From the very beginning we

conceived *D&D*'s role as being promotional and obser-
vational, rather than in any way representative. At no
point have we claimed to, or wished to, speak on behalf
of a communities movement. A line we have attempted
to tread carefully and considerately over the years.

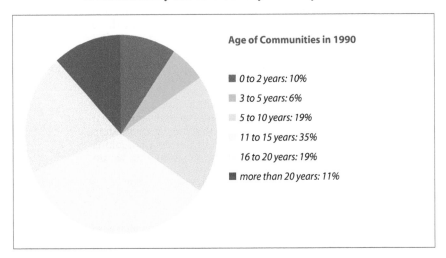

Age of Communities in 1990

■ *0 to 2 years: 10%*

■ *3 to 5 years: 6%*

■ *5 to 10 years: 19%*

11 to 15 years: 35%

16 to 20 years: 19%

■ *more than 20 years: 11%*

Initially *D&D* came under the Communes Network
umbrella with the three early editions coming out as
Communes Network publications. The Network had
thrived through the late 70's and early 80's, running a
variety of events: legal structures seminars; women in
communities weekends; readers' meetings; international
community conferences and an annual inter-community
volleyball championship. At it's peak it produc two or
three issues of the *Network* magazine a year. In the early
90's it became harder and harder to find groups willing
to do the editorial work and the magazine ended up
being put out by an ever smaller circle of communities.
Slowly subscriptions dwindled so that in the end it was
insolvent – owing more issues to subscribers than it had
money to produce. By 1993 the *D&D* editorial group
had de facto become the face of Communes Network.
In the absence of anyone else we were answering the
mail, and with increasing gaps between editions of the
magazine (and the knowledge that CN was insolvent)
we were becoming more and more embarrassed at taking people's subscription money under, what seemed
to us to be, false pretences. So at the 1994 Community
Volleyball Games a meeting was called to "officially"
wind up the Network. Reactions at the meeting ranged
from "Communes What? ...never heard of it", "I thought

it finished years ago!" to a feeling of sadness for the passing of a once loved friend. Subscribers were either sent their money back or offered a copy of *D&D*.

Since then, and somewhat to our surprise, we have become the public face of communal living in the UK. We brought out a new edition of the book every other year throughout the 90's with an updated directory listing a growing number of communities from across the UK in each edition and a new collection of articles from contributors who included as well as those living in communities, academics and writers such as Colin Ward.

Over the years the *D&D* editorial group has been made up of present and past members of different communities around the country, always remaining a small task-focused group of around 4 or 5 people. After surviving for twenty years we described ourselves as "a self-appointed-headless-elite-anarchist-editorial collective with no office, elastic editorial policies, concertina finances and a can-do/why-not attitude problem."

> *"For a number of years we held our quarterly editorial and production meetings at each others' communities. Then partly out of boredom, but mostly curiosity, we rather cheekily started asking places that we fancied visiting if they would host us. To our pleasant surprise pretty much all the places we have contacted have been more than happy for us to hide away – in one of their spare rooms for a weekend in exchange for our Communities slide show and a bit of inter-commune gossip..."*
> Writing, Printing (& Editing)
> *D&D 08/09 20th Anniversary Edition*

At the begining of the new millenium we launched ourselves on the internet at diggersanddreamers.org.uk and for several years produced directory-only books. After our 20th anniversary edition in 2008/09 we went virtual and stopped producing a printed directory – this was largely on the basis that a web based directory could be kept much more up-to-date than a book which came out every two years.

We were aware that in-effect giving away information for free could mean that at some point we would run out of money to produce anything at all. We had a plan to produce other publications (that would sit alongside the website) which we hoped would bring in enough income to keep us solvent. These have included books on the history of communal living: *Utopia Britannica* and *Communes Britannica* and more recently themed reviews on different forms of communal living: *Cohousing in Britain* and *Low-Impact Living Communities in Britain*.

But we still keep getting requests for a book which contains a printed directory! As well as this printed directories may well prove to be more robust depositories of historical information than ever-changing web-based databases.

So, somewhat out of nostagia but also as a snapshot of the present to send to the future... here we are with our 25th anniversary edition. Thank you for purchasing it and keeping going the tradition of recording communal living activity in Britain.

"Anyone who reads this guide is almost sure to start dreaming a little even if they don't get as far as digging."
The Friend 2000

"The popular image of a commune is of a group of idealistic hippies turning their backs on the world and sharing everything from their brown rice to each others lovers. But today's commune members don't look so way out. The values they espouse are general concerns..."
Good Housekeeping 1996

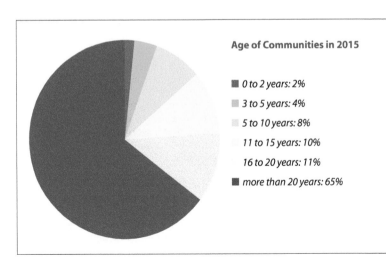

Age of Communities in 2015

- 0 to 2 years: 2%
- 3 to 5 years: 4%
- 5 to 10 years: 8%
- 11 to 15 years: 10%
- 16 to 20 years: 11%
- more than 20 years: 65%

The Digging Bit

CHRIS COATES, SARAH BUNKER, JONATHAN HOW

So you think you want to live communally?
Should you join an existing community?
How do you go about setting a new group up?
Where do you start and where will it all end?
Well you would think that the Diggers & Dreamers editors
would know a thing or two about how to go about it!

A few years ago, we thought that a how-to book on communal living would be useful, since the only UK-specific books available were *The Collective Housing Handbook* by Sarah Eno and Dave Treanor (1982), *Buying Your Own Home With Other People* by Dave Treanor (1987), both somewhat dated and hard to get hold of, and the Radical Routes booklet *How to Set Up a Housing Co-operative* (updated fairly regularly). We imagined a book which looked at all aspects of communal living, from the dream to setting up and sustaining a collective life. We began writing back in 2006, but got side-tracked by other publications.

For a while the material we had gathered appeared as a wiki section on our website and now almost a decade after we started gathering in the collected wisdom of the Diggers & Dreamers diaspora we thought it was finally time to make at least some of it available in print.

We have concentrated on how to visit and join an existing group – how to set up a new group would take a whole book on it's own. We hope that the information here is useful to the widest possible cross section of people interested in communal living. Whether you are looking for a rural farming community or want to live in an urban activists' housing co-op, we hope that you will find the information here useful to you.

So what is an intentional community?

Quite what constitutes an intentional community has been widely debated in both academic circles and amongst participants. Groups that now fall under the umbrella heading of 'intentional communities' have in the past variously been called, amongst other things: 'communes', 'communal experiments', 'utopian communities', 'utopian experiments' 'model villages,' 'land colonies' and 'alternative societies'. Today this list would also include: cohousing projects, eco-villages, low-impact living groups, housing co-operatives, ashrams and religious retreat houses.

Wikipedia, the online encyclopaedia, says an intentional community is:

> *"a planned residential community with a much higher degree of social interaction than other communities. The members of an intentional community typically hold a common social, political or spiritual vision and share responsibilities and resources."*

A more refined description comes from American academic Lyman Tower Sargent who defines an intentional community as:

> *"a group of five or more adults and their children, if any, who come from more than one nuclear family and who have chosen to live together to enhance their shared values or for some other mutually agreed upon purpose". He goes on to say that – "... they are the homes of social dreamers and that they are founded in discontent with the now and their members are deeply critical of the status quo."*[1]

More recent research in the UK by Lucy Sargisson from the School of Politics at the University of Nottingham has placed the various strands of communal living in a wider utopian context. It is her view that intentional communities are:

> *"groups of people who have chosen to live (and sometimes work) together for some common purpose. Their raison d'être goes beyond tradition, personal relationships or family ties. They are places where people try alternatives and try to live their dreams on a daily basis"*[2]

Perhaps the simplest definition comes from Andy Wood who, when trying to paint a broad picture of the various communal ventures in the UK in the first *Diggers & Dreamers Guide to Communal Living* said:

> *"Very generally, communal living can be described as situations in which people knowingly and willingly share aspects of living accommodation and material goods"*[3]

As editors of *D&D* we have somewhat ducked the question 'What is an intentional community?' when considering entries for our directory, stating in the front of each directory that we have 'always decided that we should trust the groups and allow them to decide for themselves, whether or not they should be included.'

This has led to a very wide variety of groups being listed in the book over the years; from small shared households, close classic 'communes', looser village type situations, craftwork based groups, urban activist households, organic farms, groups running new age conference centres, right through to monastic orders.

We see this broad spectrum of forms and types of community as a real strength of communal living – that the same communal solutions can be applied to a whole number of seemingly very different social situations show that the basic premises and principals are robust and can clearly be successful almost whatever the motivations of the participants.

Where to start

You could do worse than starting off by asking yourself exactly what it is that you want from communal living. What is your vision, if you have one, of your ideal community? Having a vision has always been a bit of a double-edged blessing. On the one hand visions can inspire people to greater things – to try to make the world a better place. But they can also elicit ridicule and sarcasm. Visions are also located on the border between sanity and insanity. They are what mystics and mental patients have. There is also, today, a lot of mistrust of grand visions, too many bold plans for brave new worlds have either failed to materialise or have turned out to have a lead lining to their silver clouds.

The next step is to see if anywhere can possibly live up to your vision. You've surfed the websites, read a few articles on cohousing or low-impact living and flicked through the directories – mentally crossing off half the groups because: they have the wrong diet; don't or do keep animals; are too spiritual or not spiritual enough; or maybe they appear far too idealistic or too down-to-earth for you taste. What should you do now?

Arranging your first visit to an intentional community may feel like a big deal. Will they like me? Will I like them? Will it be as good as it sounds? What will I have to do? Am I ready for this?

Don't fret too much. The reality is that at any one time there are a number of communities actively seeking

Classic big house community

In many ways the communities set up in country houses of various sizes have become the archetypal 'communes' of popular imagination. The surplus of small to medium-sized country houses in the UK after WWII meant that they became a particular feature of the British communal living scene – much more so than in other countries. Many of them went through a similar pattern of: wealthy family-owned country house -> wartime forces requisition -> life as some kind of institution (hospital/nursing home etc) -> sell-off relatively cheaply when they became either unfit for their purpose or the maintenance bills got too high for the authorities. At this point they were purchased by budding communards. Other houses came on the market through farm amalgamation or through sales to cover death duties. The 'hey-day' of the big house commune is seen as the 1970's, but they can be found popping up from the late 1940's through to the early 1990's when they became increasingly attactive to property developers who could convert them to "character" accommodation. This took selling prices beyond the reach of communal groups. The occasional big house still manages to make an appearance despite the obstacle of obscene 21st century house prices.

Examples in the directory might be Birchwood, Bowden House, Laurieston Hall and Redfield.

Your ideal community

The following exercise may assist you to clarify your personal community vision. Take a sheet of paper and some crayons or felt-tipped pens, and draw a simple sketch, map, or diagram of your ideal community. It might be a good idea to represent your personal space as a small square in the center of the page. We're not concerned here with the details of your house or apartment, but rather with what is around it. Start to put in other houses or buildings, roughly indicating how far apart they are:

- Do you want to see other houses from your own, or do you want to be in a rural setting?

- Do you imagine yourself and others in this setting mostly driving back and forth to home, or do you imagine walking to some places? What would those be – a park, a beach, a church, a grocery store, a coffee shop? How close would you like these to be?

- If you have children, how close might they like to be? What about when they are teenagers: Are you prepared to drive them everywhere they want to go, or would you like them to have the freedom to walk to shops or take the bus to the library?

- How urban – or rural – do you imagine your ideal community to be? Do you want uninterrupted views of farmland or mountains, or do you like to see houses, and people passing by through the filtered greenery of street trees?

- What about privacy? Some people like to be able to avoid others and have time to themselves and their immediate family. Others enjoy seeing people and may seek out situations as an "excuse" to chat with neighbours or passersby.

- What kind of house-world connection appeals to you?

- What level of privacy from the outside world do you require to feel comfortable?

- How far are you willing to commute to work? Put an arrow on your drawing to indicate the time it would take you to get to work from this community. If you'd ideally like to walk to work, what are you willing to compromise on in order to do that?

- What kind of exercise or recreation appeals to you? If you like to go to a yoga class or to work-out or play squash with a friend, how close to home (or work) would you like this amenity to be? If you like to walk or cycle from home, how close would you like a footpath or cycletrack to be?

Don't let yourself be sidetracked by a rational judge in your head who says "Oh come on! You can't really have everything you want." Although your ideal community might not exist in all the particulars you have outlined, you may be surprised at how many of the qualities you value can be found in an existing place. Once you have really thought about the kind of setting in which you would feel totally "at home," go exploring and look for it!

Adapted From: House as a Mirror of Self by Clare Marcus

new members and most groups that advertise themselves welcome visitors and are experienced at hosting all sorts of people. The hardest part may be deciding which group(s) you want to visit in the first place. You can try and find out as much as you can about a place before making your mind up, but the information you get may be sketchy and anyway it can be quite hard to judge a place simply from what they write about themselves. If you can't make up your mind choose two or three that seem close to what you are looking for, or a couple in the area you want to live in.

Where to start?

You could do worse than starting off by asking yourself exactly what it is that you want from visiting a community? Not what you hope to get from communal living in general (though that's useful to think about too), but what you hope to get out of visiting this particular community – what is the purpose of your visit?

- *Have you picked them out because they look like the best fit with your vision of an ideal community? Be prepared to be disappointed.*

- *Are you just curious to find out more about communal living? Perhaps you should look out for a community offering a visitor weekend where you may get a broader picture of intentional communities than you would visiting one group in isolation.*

- *Are you looking for a change in direction of your life? – think about visiting a number of different communities to see a range of possibilities.*

- *Are you looking for love and expect it will be easier to find in a community? Be prepared to be disappointed.*

It may well be worthwhile also asking yourself why a particular community is open to visitors? What do they want or need from you as a visitor? In general groups that advertise in directories are looking for people who might join them, maybe not immediately, but perhaps at some time in the future. They may be doing this on an active basis – certainly if they have vacant space to fill at the time. If you have seen an ad on the web or in a magazine you can assume that they are positively looking for new members. On the other hand they may be being much more selective and only looking to find someone with a high degree of compatibility and expect to have to host quite a few visitors to find them. Communities may well have various other reasons for having visitors, other than looking for new members. It may be that they simply need help with their work – either on a seasonal basis or ongoing. A number of groups make some of their living from running conferences and seminars and may use this as a way of getting to know visitors who then turn into prospective members.

Some of the more organized groups host visitors because they are interested in spreading their philosophy or religion – don't be put off by this – especially if you have sympathy with their ideas. Some isolated groups may just welcome the stimulation and company of outsiders. What is fairly certain is that a community which open its doors to strangers on a regular basis is doing it for its own reasons and needs, and only rarely just for reasons of hospitality.

In some instances a group that is undergoing stressful changes, or is simply overloaded with work will continue to host visitors when you might think that what they needed was a break from meeting new people. Often they are doing this due to a sense of mission or obligation, or because they need to get more members to reduce their workload and stress. If you find yourself arriving in this situation – tread carefully – you may find that it is only the visitor coordinator and a few others who are welcoming. Some community members may well appear distant and keep a low profile during your visit.Try not to take it too personally! It is probable that they are quietly getting on with keeping the community together and

"A mistake to be avoided is treating communities like a sort of Disney World, put there for the interest of the public. For the most part, intentional communities are not showcases, are not kept up to impress outsiders, and are not particularly interested in being looked at by casual tourists. Resident communitarians may put up with a certain amount of tourism for income, or for outreach; but residents live their personal lives in community, and generally they don't enjoy uninvolved spectators."

Kat Kincade, then a member of Twin Oaks Community, USA

don't have any spare energy for new people. Visitor overload and politeness burnout can also happen to some community members at the best of times as well. Coping with a regular stream of strangers visiting your home can just get overwhelming – communities are aware of this and some arrange organised tours and visitor weekends to cope with it.

Arranging to Visit

The two most usual routes to arranging a visit to a community are through personal acquaintance with an existing member (or perhaps through a friend-of-a-friend) and by writing. If you are able to arrange a

Land-based communities

"Back to the land!" has been the rallying call of communards for centuries from the 17th century Diggers, through the Chartist land settlements and the Anarchist land colonies to the present Low Impact developments. Buying land and establishing a successful land based community have not proved easy and the number of groups making a living off the land is small. Most supplementing their income with outside jobs. There are a number of communal models for land settlement. There are a few communities that in effect manage to run a small farm or smallholding alongside other activities, there are groups living in woodland focusing their activities on woodland management and there are groups living in tipis, benders and yurts often slipping under the radar of local planners or battling with them for the right to live on the land.

See: Old Hall, Steward Wood, Tipi Valley for examples.

Low Impact Living Communities in Britain

A Diggers & Dreamers Review

Take a look at our more specialised publication

visit through a personal contact then you may find that your initial visit is easy to arrange – though don't be put off if you are asked to write a 'formal' letter to introduce yourself – or are asked to come through the group's usual visitor procedures. Regardless of whether you are writing to a group whose address you have got from an ad in a magazine or directory, or you are responding via the group's website then, inevitably, getting the balance of your letter, or email, right can be tricky. You don't want to write too much or too little. Aim for a maximum of two pages – anything longer and you run the risk of getting put in the 'needs-to-be-answered-but-requires-a-lot-of-time-and-energy-to-deal-with-file' and this seriously reduces the chances of you getting a prompt reply. Try to avoid just writing a long list of questions about the community and remember to include plenty of information about who you are and what you're seeking. Whilst there is no formula that will guarantee that your letter will appeal to any particular group, and you should write in whatever your own personal style is, a good aim would be to give equal emphasis to:

- *describing what you're looking for, how you heard about them, and why they interest you;*
- *telling them about your history, skills, and special needs*
- *posing questions about the community and how to visit*

If you're writing using snail-mail make sure you enclose a stamp addressed envelope (SAE).

What happens to your letter (or e-mail)?

Chances are that your letter will be opened and dealt with by someone whose 'job' or role it is to respond to enquiries – a visitor co-ordinator or group secretary. They may be delegated to reply directly, especially if the group runs dedicated visitor weekends for which little or no pre-selection is carried out. In which case you may just get a fairly standard reply and invitation to join in with an organised visitor programme. If the group has a more informal approach to visitors there may well be some approval process that your request has to go through – this could be as simple as being pinned up on a notice board for members to read and comment on before the secretary responds or it may go to a meeting for discussion. Some groups require visitors to be sponsored or hosted by a particular member before a visit can be agreed and you may well get a personal letter from your host if this is the case. These processes can take a while so don't expect to get a reply by return of post or email. Also in spite of good intentions the sad truth is that many groups don't respond to letters at all promptly. Living in community can be very demanding – there's always so much to be done – and answering a stack of correspondence doesn't usually rank as high on the chore list as milking the cows, supervising the kids, taking out the recycling, or building the new compost loo!

If you don't get a reply after three or four weeks then try following up with a quick phone call, if you have the group's number. Catching someone on a communal phone can be a somewhat hit-and-miss affair. Early evenings, or right before or after a meal, are good times to try. If you get an answering machine then leave your number and ask them to call you back at their convenience. Suggest times when you're most reachable, and explain that when they do get through, you'd be happy to hang up and call them right back at your expense. If you strike it lucky first time and a real live person picks up the phone don't assume that they will know all about you. Introduce yourself, mention that you've already sent a letter, and explain that you're interested in visiting. Be sure to ask whoever has picked up the phone if they're a good person to talk with about visiting, and check that this is a good time to talk. If not get a contact name and offer to call back at another time. If you are patient and persistent you should be able to get through in the end.

What to expect on a first visit

So what can you expect when – having packed your sleeping bag, wellies, working clothes and hot water bottle – you find yourself at the door of your chosen community?

The first task that a visitor to a community faces is to find the door that everyone uses; not usually the most obvious-looking entrance, or the first one that you come across. The next is to find a friendly face or, come to that, any face! You could find yourself wandering down seemingly endless corridors following the faint sound of distant voices or that singing that seems to

Cohousing

Starting in Scandinavia in the 1970's cohousing has now become an increasingly popular model for setting up community. The classic cohousing development aims to be purpose designed mini-neighbourhood where people have their own self-contained accommodation and personal space as well as sharing communal facilities. They have a common house at the centre of the community where members can meet for meals and socialise. UK groups have found it difficult to get off the ground mainly due to the problems in finding suitable land or property that they can afford.

See: Springhill, Laughton Lodge, LILAC and Forgebank for examples

Cohousing in Britain

Take a look at our more specialised publication

A Diggers & Dreamers Review

"Shall I be on my best behaviour while I visit, or shall I let them know what I am really like? By all means put your best foot forward! The experienced community makes allowances. We know that in a year or two you're not going to be jumping up and volunteering to wash the dishes, the way you did when you were visiting. But the eagerness to make a good impression makes a good impression. We'll like you wanting to please. It says something good about your social skills. We know that the real you is somewhat more of a mixed bag. So is the real us for that matter."

Kat Kincade, then a member of Twin Oaks Community, USA

be coming from just the other side of the wall. Don't Panic. Whether members work in the community or in outside jobs, chances are they are busy and it is only the bigger groups that are able to have someone dedicated to welcoming visitors.

Persevere, try the back door. In 'Big House' communities people tend to gravitate towards the smaller-scale service or old servant quarters that are generally easier to heat and more human-scale. Leaving the large rooms that you have just wandered through for use for meetings, dining rooms or as spaces for courses and the odd party. Still no Luck? Then head for the kitchen. Like any home, much social life in an intentional

Urban housing co-ops and house-shares

Many housing co-ops have a history dating back to the squatting movement of the 1970s. They may well now be less communal in their nature but still uphold the tradition of shared ownership and control. In the last few decades a whole new wave of housing co-ops have been formed with the help of the organisation known as Radical Routes – these generally are more communal. A brand new development has been student housing co-ops. In addition to all this there are many house-shares which often don't have any legal structure but with the right people on-board can be very viable.

See: Sanford Housing Co-op, Cornerstone, Edinburgh Student Housing Co-op and Oakleigh for examples.

community revolves around the kitchen. Communal meals, as much as formal meetings, are where ideas and decisions are thrashed out and mass catering is a skill much appreciated. Still found no one? Then put the kettle on and wait for someone to turn up. Of course if you've booked into an organised visitor weekend you can expect a friendly face to greet you and a hot cup of something when you arrive.

Groups often have spare rooms for visitors and guests, these can range from fairly basic hostel style to quite nice hotel standard accommodation. But if they are pushed for space you may find yourself in the personal room of a member who happens to be away – so it's best to be prepared and to treat the spaces with respect. Most groups make a modest charge to cover food and accommodation on your initial visit; if there is an organised visitor programme the cost may be slightly higher. On subsequent and longer visits charges may well be negotiable.

Making yourself useful on your visit can be done in a whole variety of ways. Offer to help with everyday tasks such as gardening, farm work, construction projects, cooking, cleaning, washing dishes, childcare. You may gain "Much Appreciated Guest" status if you have special skills to offer: layout or graphic design, DIY and building skills, computer skills, furniture repairs, storytelling, music, massage... Often, however, the most appreciated contribution is your willingness to pitch in to help with whatever boring chore needs doing at the moment. Sometimes though groups are not organised in a way that lets visitors join in easily and your desire to help can actually become more of a headache for them than a help. Use your intuition in such situations. Make suggestions, but be open – offer, but don't push too hard. If they aren't able to involve you in the work and don't have much time to spend with you, be prepared to entertain yourself: bring books, CDs, musical instruments, etc.

Visiting communities can be a bit like dating – people on both sides can have a tendency to put their best foot forward and try to hide what they consider to be weaknesses. You are also unlikely to get to know all aspects of a community on a 'first-date'. Try and be aware of what you may have missed. Did you get to see the group at a meeting? Were there members that you didn't meet? Did you only visit during the week when everyone was working or vice versa? Did you see how they deal with a challenging issue?

To dig deeper, learn how to ask friendly but penetrating questions. After you've got to know a new group well enough to get more personal, try posing such open-ended queries as:

- *What are some of the things you like best about living here? The least?*

- *What's the most difficult issue your community has had to deal with in the last year, or in the last five years?*

- *How many members have left in the past year or two, and why did they leave?*

Tips to help your visit go smoothly

1   Always remember: the community you're visiting is also somebody's home, so plan on using the same standards you'd use if you were visiting friends or relatives you see only occasionally

2   Avoid treating communities like some sort of theme park put there for the interest of the public. For the most part, intentional communities are not showcases and are not kept up to impress outsiders.

3   Nothing opens doors better, nothing generates more trust and mutual understanding, than simply working together.

4   Try to develop a nose for "landmines" you are liable to put your foot into in the course of a project's daily life. Try to avoid them but if you do tread on one, don't take it too personally – it happens to everyone.

5   If you have a dog (or other pet for that matter) don't assume that it's OK just to turn up with it – check it out beforehand.

6   Observe written or oral instructions, even when their meaning is not immediately apparent (but if in doubt feel free to ask why things are done in the way they are).

7   Nothing is more obnoxious than the visitor who defies the important traditions of a community – A certain amount of "When in Rome do as the Romans do," is usually appropriate.

8   Remember the community you see during any one visit is not the whole community

- How has the community changed over the years? What changes would you like to see in the future?

- What are some of the big challenges your community is facing now?

- How has living here contributed to your personal growth and happiness?

- What is the procedure for accepting new members?

- What are the arrangements for leaving the community?

- How would you describe the social structure of the community?

- What would you say was the main focus of the community?

- What is the community's legal structure?

- How much communal work is expected from members?

- What are the unwritten rules of the community?

- What is the process of decision making in the community?

- How does the community deal with conflict?

- Has the community and its buildings received local government approval?

- What is the age distribution of people living in the community?

It's probably an excellent idea not to fire off all these questions at once!

If the community members perceive you as being sincere, interested, and open minded, most will be willing to engage with you in a thoughtful dialogue. However, if they sense that you've already made up your mind about what's right—and are likely to pass judgment on them when they fall short of your expectations—not much information will be forthcoming. You can learn a lot from talking with other visitors as they may have picked up on things that you have missed. Those living in other communities can give a different perspective as well... that's definitely one of the advantages of visiting more than one group.

"What gets our backs up about visitors? Well some do seem to forget that they're in someone's (Many people's) home and it's not pleasant to have your home treated like an institution. We're not generally frightened of being criticised or challenged, but there's a limit and it helps if first there is an attempt to not only understand how thing are but also why."

Dave Green, then a member of Crabapple

What happens after I've visited?

Once you've got through your first visit you'll probably have a better idea of what you're looking for. It's often good to spend some time away from the group after a first visit just to see if your initial impressions hold up. It can be particularly interesting and informative to listen to yourself answer questions about the community posed by your pre-community friends and acquaintances.

If you decide that you want to visit again the process will vary from place to place so make sure you have asked what happens next before you leave. Usually the group will want to discuss it amongst themselves. You have every right to demand clarity, but try to be understanding of any difficulties that a group may have in coming to a decision about you.

"At one time when considering new members we used to be on the lookout for couples who were trying to give their shaky relationship one last chance by joining a community. We thought this was bad news and that we would end up picking up the pieces after an inevitable relationship breakdown. This would result in one if not both of the couple leaving anyway leaving a trail of emotionally exhausted members in their wake. Looking back I can see that we were being a little harsh and judgemental – communal set ups can be relatively safe places for relationships to split up, not just for couples coming in but for long term members – if you can stand seeing your ex at breakfast that is."
Chris Coates, then a member of People in Common

Your impression, as an outsider, may well be of a unified "them" against you. The reality is much more likely to be that there is a spread of views within the group; and the thing that takes time is the group trying to come to a consensus.

When you become a member yourself you will appreciate what they went through!

If some members are unsure about you it will probably not enhance their opinion of you to be put under pressure. It is all much more complicated than going for a job interview – these people are going to have to share their lives with you and you with them. So allow time for the process. Some communities will offer a probationary period – perhaps three or six months. Others will require you to make more and longer visits but (If and when they decide positively) may give full membership straight away. There are good and bad sides to both systems.

If a community doesn't want you to return or turns down your membership after a number of visits, try not to take it too personally, it could be for any number of reasons. The group may be full, it may be looking to address a gender balance and you just happen to be not what they are looking for, it may be that there were a number of people applying to join at the time and you were unlucky.

An Ounce of Prevention

There are times when, for good reasons, a group may wish to ask an existing member to leave, or may identify characteristics in potential new members that might indicate a high risk of their generating later conflict. The sense of community and connection that a group of people can co-create is both valuable and vulnerable. It is the responsibility of each member who values the community to nourish and protect it. There may be a conflict between nourishing and protecting: nourishing can mean bringing in new fertilizer, new members with new perspectives, enthusiasms, and energy; protecting can involve not accepting risky new people. Each community must find its own balance point between risk and safety. This balance point may change over time, as the needs and strengths of the group vary. At any given time, a group's physical and interpersonal resources are limited; choosing carefully which people (and how many) to try to integrate can make the most efficient use of these limited resources. In my experience, "red flags" for high risk occur in potential new members who:

● have not gotten their financial trip together before they come,

● want to get away from it all,

● expect that living in community will be easy

● must have everything they want in terms of physical comfort, work assignments; and so forth soon after joining the community;

● have few or no ongoing connections to family; friends, or people from their previous living and working arrangements,

● appear to be "hiding from themselves",

● lie or steal,

● blame everybody/everything else for their problems and/or failures, are looking for authority figures to rebel against.

From: Community Member As Lightning Rod by Harvey Baker

If a community that you really like is full they may operate a waiting pool of people who know what their place is like and "might move in some day." However, as hosting visitors can be tiring and energy-consuming you'll find that some communities put up the barricades when they're full because there seems no immediate need to find new members. It's always worth asking to be kept informed if a place comes up.

If you don't find a community that suits you, or you don't suit it, don't give up keep on looking for a place where you will fit in. Try different ways of visiting: try a wwoof (World Wide Opportinities on Organic Farms) weekend or go on one of the organised visitor weekend which some groups run. Try looking through the Forming Groups part of our online directory and see if you can work with others set up a new community. Hopefully you will find somewhere.

Good Luck!

The Communal Back Door

Having outlined the various 'official' ways to go about visiting and joining a community it has to be said that it is highly likely that most groups have had one or more members who have managed to bypass some of or even the entire official route and got in through the back door. There is not necessarily anything wrong going on here – and from the community's point of view letting new members in through the 'back door' can turn out to be just as successful as those coming through the front. The sort of 'off-road' routes that some people find lead them to an intentional community include; having a relationship with an community member, being family, being a neighbour, working with a community member, meeting community members in a different context say at an evening class and getting to know them first that way, coming from another community...

Useful Books

- BAKER , B, *With a Little Help from Our Friends: Creating Community as We Grow Older*. Vanderbilt University Press; (2014) ISBN-13: 978-0826519887

- BUNKER, S et al (eds), *Cohousing in Britain: A Diggers & Dreamers Review*. Diggers and Dreamers Publications (2011) ISBN-13: 978-0954575731

- BUNKER, S et al (eds), *Low Impact Living Communities in Britain: A Diggers & Dreamers Review*. Diggers and Dreamers Publications (2014) ISBN-13: 978-0954575748

- CHATTERTON, P, *Low Impact Living: A Field Guide to Ecological, Affordable Community Building*. Routledge (2014) ISBN-13: 978-0415661614

- DURRETT, C, *The Senior Cohousing Handbook: A Community Approach to Independent Living*. New Society Publishers; (2nd edition 2009) ISBN-13: 978-0865716117

- HALL, J, *Is This The Future? An Investigation Into Communal Living*. lulu.com (2012) ISBN-13: 978-1447709367

- HULSE, J, *Communal Living: The Ultimate Guide for Communal Living And What You Need to Know*. CreateSpace Independent Publishing Platform (2014) ISBN-13: 978-1507888407

- JANZEN, D, *Intentional Christian Community Handbook*. Paraclete Press (2012) ISBN-13: 978-1612612379

- JONES, J, *A Place of Refuge: An Experiment in Communal Living - The Story of Windsor Hill Wood.* Quercus (2015)
  ISBN-13: 978-1848662483

- JONES, J, *Utopian Dreams.* Faber & Faber (2008)
  ISBN-13: 978-0571223817

- LEACH, S, *Head, Heart & Hands.* Johnson Printing (2005). Available from: www.ic.org/community-bookstore

- LEAFE CHRISTIAN, D, *Creating a Life Together: Practical Tools to Grow Ecovillages and Intentional Communities.* New Society Publishers (2003)
  ISBN-13: 978-0865714717

- LEAFE CHRISTIAN, D, *Finding Community: How to Join an Ecovillage or Intentional Community.* New Society Publishers (2007)
  ISBN-13: 978-0865715783

- McCAMANT, K and DURRETT, C, *Creating Cohousing: Building Sustainable Communities.* New Society Publishers, (2011)
  ISBN-13: 978-0865716728

- MELTZER, G, *Findhorn Reflections: A very personal take on life inside the famous spiritual community and ecovillage.* CreateSpace Independent Publishing Platform (2015)
  ISBN-13: 978-1512006513

- PLUHAR, A, *Sharing Housing: A Guidebook for Finding and Keeping Good Housemates.* Homemate Publishing; (2nd edition (2011)
  ISBN-13: 978-0991010400

- SAWTELL, R, *Under One Roof: The story of a Christian community.* Darton,Longman & Todd Ltd (2015)
  ISBN-13: 978-0232531732

- SEEDS FOR CHANGE, *A Consensus Handbook: Co-operative Decision Making for Activists, Co-ops and Communities.* Seeds for Change Lancaster Co-operative Ltd (2013) ISBN-13: 978-0957587106

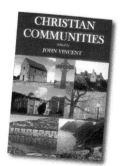

- VINCENT, J (ed), *Christian Communities.* Ashram Press (2011) ISBN-13: 978-0955907326

- WEAVER, E, *Let's Talk About Money: A Conversation Guide for Intentional Communities.* CreateSpace Independent Publishing Platform (2011) ISBN-13: 978-1478148647

- WIMBUSH, P, *The Birth of an Ecovillage.* FeedaRead.com (2012) ISBN-13: 978-1781764923

- WURFEL, M, *eurotopia: Living in Community: Directory of Communities and Ecovillages in Europe.* Einfach Gut Leben (2013) ISBN-13: 978-3981296822

Useful Websites

- Camphill England and Wales
  www.camphill.org.uk

- Camphill Northern Ireland
  www.camphillni.org

- Camphill Scotland
  www.camphillscotland.org.uk

- Camphill Village Trust
  www.cvt.org.uk

- Confederation of Co-operative Housing
  www.cch.coop

- Gaia Eco-villages Network
  www.gaia.org

- International Communal Studies Association
  www.communa.org.il/icsa

- Students for Co-operation
  www.students.coop

- UK Cohousing Network
  www.cohousing.org.uk

- Rhizome
  rhizomenetwork.wordpress.com

- Co-operative and Community Finance
  www.coopfinance.coop

- Co-operatives UK
  www.cooperatives-uk.coop

- Ecology Building Society
  www.ecology.co.uk

- Radical Routes
  www.radicalroutes.org.uk

- Rootstock
  www.rootstock.org.uk

- Triodos Bank
  www.triodos.co.uk

- Permaculture Association
  www.permaculture.org.uk

- Permanent Publications
  www.permaculture.co.uk

- World Wide Opportunities on Organic Farms
  www.wwoof.org.uk

- LowImpact.org
  www.lowimpact.org

- This Land is Ours
  www.tlio.org.uk

Directory of Communities in Britain

Since 1990 Diggers & Dreamers has provided the definitive listing of British communities. We are now almost completely web-based but the demand for a printed edition goes on...!

One of the reasons that we have moved towards having an online directory is that the printed listings start to go out of date almost the minute that the book hits the streets. However... there remains a persistent demand for a printed directory. Sometimes from web-refuseniks; sometimes from apocalypse-anticipators who want to be prepared; sometimes from people who are aware that there remain a lot of internet not-spots; but most often – we suspect – from people who just like to have something solid in their hands!

We want to make you aware of some of the issues which come up in producing a directory like this. Where membership of a group has changed they are often keen to ditch earlier "outdated blurb that doesn't in any way reflect what's going on now". They're keen to respond so we love them! However, getting some communities to update their entries can be like extracting blood from a stone. Members may be keener on just getting on with the business of communal living and don't want to spend any more time than they have to writing about it. Perhaps a community that has spent a long time in a past year crafting a written description (which they can all finally agree on) is now reluctant to change it just for the sake of looking different. So if a community's entry seems quite similar to what you might have read in the past then it doesn't mean that absolutely nothing has changed!

We asked groups to consciously opt in to having a full entry in this book so the places that have full page listings have done just that. However, there were others (that we know still to exist) which have not responded at all but, at the time of writing, have a full entry on our website directory. For completeness we've included just their names and postcodes in a list at the end. For the most up-to-date information take a look at the Directory pages of diggersanddreamers.org.uk where communities can keep their own entries current.

When you start to read the entries, you will notice that there is a wide variety of types of communal living groups; some of these groups may work together, some may share income, some may have a spiritual focus, some may not necessarily live under the same roof; whole groups, or people within the groups, may be committed to ideals such as permaculture, veganism, home education and struggling against sexism, racism and homophobia; others may well not.

Remember that there are also many other communal groups which are not listed at all, including countless shared houses. All the groups in this directory, however, share a desire to be public (to a greater or lesser degree) about their lifestyle; some may be looking for new members, and most of them will welcome visitors. If you are thinking about living communally and want to experience what these places are like, this is where to start. If you do decide that you want to visit one or more places, then please bear in mind the points described in the earlier "Digging Bit" article. And whatever you do, please don't just turn up. Remember that you will be going into people's homes, and it is important to write to them – letting them know why you are interested in their particular place – then waiting for an invitation to come.

How to use the Index, Map and Directory

The Index on pages 114 and 115 is intended to help you select the groups you may wish to visit. We have tried, as far as possible, to go by groups' own answers to the questions. A ● is only shown if their answer was definitely "yes". If their answer was "no" or ambiguous then nothing is shown. In such cases it might mean, for example, that they do share income in some way or that they do eat communally occasionally.

A letter denotes those communities with a spiritual focus:

A Anthroposophy (philosophy of Rudolf Steiner)
B Buddhist
C Christian
Q Quaker
S Spiritual but non-specific

The numbers on both the index and the map refer to the page number of each group's entry. Entries are ordered alphabetically and names may be abridged in the index.

Quite a lot of groups do not wish their telephone numbers to be published and some groups did not want their addresses printed. Please contact them by e-mail as we are unable to forward mail.

The question 'Open to new members?' is about the general principle rather than the current status. Only a group that is closed indefinitely will answer "no". However, a group which is open to new members (and therefore answers "yes") may not necessarily have any space at the time you contact them. Before making contact it's worth consulting the Places needing Members section on the D&D website – this is intended to give a more immediate picture of which communities are currently looking for new members and is usually reasonably up-to-date.

Some groups set aside particular dates for showing round first-time visitors while yet others welcome volunteers and/or WWOOFers. The Places needing Volunteers section on the website will guide you towards these communities that are actively seeking volunteers and we would always recommend joining WWOOF. The Index on pages 114 and 115 shows which communities are also WWOOF hosts.

In addition to being communities, many places also run centres with full workshop programmes – sometimes member-led and sometimes run by external tutors who are hiring the facilities. Attending such workshops may well be a good way of having a peep at a community for the first time, but don't necessarily expect to get the full flavour of day-to-day communal life from the experience. Better are courses that are specifically about communal living. At the time of writing, the most regular of these are the Living in Community Weekends held at Redfield in Buckinghamshire and the Experience Weeks held very frequently at the Findhorn Foundation in Morayshire. Other places have also run "induction" type events in the past. In addition many communities welcome people to stay during their annual maintenance weeks. But don't see this as a way of getting a free lunch and if you feel outrage at being charged to stay during such times, do remember that the members are also having to pay to live there *and* do maintenance!

Most importantly – don't be shy. Groups rely on a stream of visitors to find the new members that are essential for the ongoing life of the community, and a wealth of experiences await you!

The Icons decoded

Land and Food

 land management programme, members expected to help look after the land

 grow a lot of vegetables – substantial garden (but not necessarily self-sufficient)

 animals reared for food – livestock reared for human consumption

 regular communal meals

Smoking and Access

 policy which restricts smoking – smoking restricted to certain areas or banned

 wheelchair access

Transport

 regular use of bikes for transport

 shared use of vehicles – car pool or recognised arrangements for sharing private cars

 easy access to public transport – bus stop and/or train station within easy walking distance

Resources

 shared utilities – domestic facilities (eg washing machines) shared

 shared workshop – communal workshop and communally owned tools

 organised recycling system

 eco-friendly sewage system – compost toilets, reed beds or other alternatives in use

 broadband internet access available – possibly networked

Money

 income sharing community – all income is shared

 capital required – capital required from all members

Energy Use

 on site electricity generation – wind, water or solar energy provides some power

 solar power used – solar used for space and/or water heating

 insulation to a high standard – buildings are double-glazed and insulated

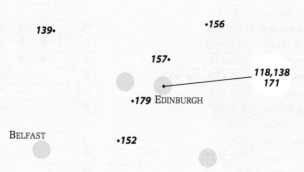
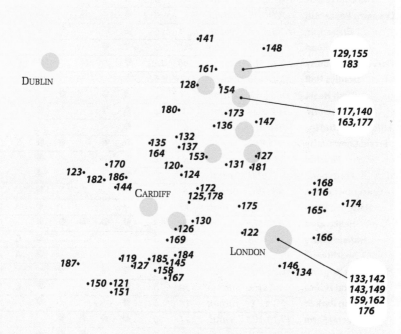

188.•160

139•

•156

157•

118,138
171

•179 EDINBURGH

BELFAST

•152

•141

•148

129,155
183

DUBLIN

161•

128•

154

180•

•173

117,140
163,177

•136   •147

•132

•135   •137

164   153•

•170   120•

123•

182• 186•

•144   CARDIFF

•131 •181

•127

•124

•172
125,178

•168
•116

165•   •174

•175

•130

•126

•169

•122

LONDON

•166

187•

•119 •185 •184

•127   •145

•158

•167

•146
•134

133,142
143,149
159,162
176

•150 •121
•151

	postcode	situation	number of adults	number of children	open to new members	charge visitors	work in lieu possible	WWOOF host	daily communal meals	spiritual focus	page
Argyle Street	CB1 3LU	urban	85	7	●				●		116
Ashram Community	S4 7AY	urban	45	0	●				●	C	117
Auchinleck	EH6 4SG	urban	7	0	●				●		118
Beech Hill	EX17 6RF	rural	12	3	●	●	●	●	●		119
Birchwood Hall	WR13 5EZ	rural	18	2	●				●		120
Bowden House	TQ9 7PW	rural	26	15	●				●		121
Braziers Community	OX10 6AN	rural	14	1	●	●	●	●	●		122
Brithdir Mawr	SA42 0QJ	rural	13	0	●		●	●	●		123
Canon Frome Court	HR8 2TD	rural	28	21	●		●	●	●		124
CoFlats Lansdown	GL5 1TN	urban	14	0	●				●		125
CoFlats Sladbrook	GL5 1TN	urban	14	0	●				●		125
Cohousing Bristol	BS3 5ES	urban	10	1	●				●		126
Corani	EX17 3BU	urban	11	0	●				●		127
Cordata Co-op	M20 3EA	urban	6	0	●				●		128
Cornerstone	LS7 3HB	urban	16	0	●				●		129
The Courtyards	BA15 2PB	rural	10	6	●				●		130
Coventry Peace Hse	CV6 5DS	urban	7	0	●			●	●		131
Crabapple	SY5 6HA	rural	10	6	●	●		●	●		132
Crescent Road	KT2 7RD	urban	20	3		●			●		133
Darvell Community	TN32 5DR	rural	160	150	●		●		●	C	134
Dol-llys Hall	SY18 6JB	rural	12	5	●				●		135
Earth Heart	DE6 1NS	rural	14	4	●	●		●			136
Earthworm	SY7 0LH	rural	9	1	●	●			●		137
Edinburgh Student	EH10 4HR	urban	106	0	●						138
Erraid Community	PA66 6BN	rural	4	2	●	●		●	●	S	139
Fireside	S3 9DN	urban	9	2	●				●		140
Forgebank	LA2 6FD	rural	61	15	●				●		141
Guiseppe Conlon	N41BG	urban	5	0	●			●	●	C	142
Hargrave Road	N19 5SJ	urban	12	0	●				●		143
Heartwood	SA17 5ES	rural	8	4	●	●	●	●	●		144
Hilfield Friary	DT2 7BE	rural	20	3	●				●	C	145
Hoathly Hill	RH19 4SJ	rural	55	15	●				●	A	146
Hockerton Housing	NG25 0QU	rural	11	9	●	●		●			147
Holy Rood House	Y07 1HX	urban	30	0	●	●			●	C	148
Islington Park St	N1 1PX	urban	18	0	●				●		149
Keveral Farm	PL13 1PA	rural	11	0	●	●	●	●			150
Landmatters	TQ9 7DL	rural	9	7			●	●	●		151

	postcode	situation	number of adults	number of children	open to new members	charge visitors	work in lieu possible	WWOOF host	daily communal meals	spiritual focus	page
Laurieston Hall	DG7 2NB	rural	20	0	●	●					152
Lee Abbey	B6 5ND	urban	5	0	●				●	C	153
Lifespan	S36 4JG	rural	20	7	●	●	●		●		154
LILAC	LS5 3AG	urban	25	6	●				●		155
Milltown	AB30 1PB	rural	15	2	●		●			A	156
Monimail	KY15 7RJ	rural	7	0	●	●		●	●		157
Monkton Wyld	DT6 6DQ	rural	8	2	●	●	●	●	●		158
Mornington Grove	E3 4NS	Urban	11	0	●				●		159
Newbold House	IV36 2RE	urban	12	0	●	●	●	●	●		160
Nutclough	HX7 8HA	rural	7	2	●	●	●		●		161
Oakfield Road	N4 4LB	urban	5	0					●		162
Oakleigh	S4 7AG	urban	8	0	●				●		163
Old Chapel Farm	SY18 6JR	rural	8		●		●	●	●		164
Old Hall Community	CO7 6TG	rural	45	9	●	●	●	●	●		165
Othona Essex	CM0 7PN	rural	5	0	●	●	●	●	●	C	166
Othona West Dorset	DT6 4RN	rural	7	0	●	●			●	C	167
Parsonage Farm	CB25	rural	4	0	●				●		168
Pendragon	BA6 8AQ	urban	9	6	●			●	●		169
Pengraig	SA44 5HX	rural	10	0	●	●	●	●	●		170
Ploughshare	EH10 4JQ	urban	8	0	●				●		171
Postlip Community	GL54 5AQ	rural	14	10	●		●	●	●		172
Quaker Community	S33 0DA	rural	9	0	●	●				Q	173
Random Camel	IP4 1BQ	urban	8	2	●				●		174
Redfield	MK18 3LZ	rural	15	8	●	●	●	●	●		175
Sanford	SE14 6NB	urban	122	0	●						176
Share Instead	S7 1DS	urban	5	0	●	●					177
Springhill	GL5 1TN	urban	50	32	●	●			●		178
Talamh	ML11 0NJ	rural	6	0	●		●	●	●		179
Taraloka	SY13 2LD	rural	12	0		●			●	B	180
Tariki Trust	LE19 2GR	rural	4	0	●	●			●	B	181
Temple Druid	SA66 7XS	rural	6	3	●	●	●		●		182
301 Housing Co-op	LS7 3JT	urban	7	0							183
Threshold Centre	SP8 5JQ	rural	19	1	●				●		184
Tinker's Bubble	TA14 6TE	rural	10	2	●	●	●	●	●		185
Tipi Valley	SA19 7EE	rural	50	30	●						186
Trelay	EX23 0NJ	rural	20	8	●	●	●		●		187
Woodhead	IV36 2UE	rural	6	0	●	●	●	●	●	S	188

Argyle St Housing Co-op

Postal Address
*3 Fletchers Terrace
Cambridge CB1 3LU*

Telephone
01223 411615

Electronic Mail
office@ash.coop

Over 18s
85

Under 18s
7

Year started
1981

Situation
urban

Ideological focus
*co-operative/communal
living*

Legal structure
*fully mutual housing
co-operative*

Open to new members?
yes

Charge visitors?
no

Work in lieu?
no

Argyle Street Housing Co-operative opened in 1981 as a "fully mutual" co-op. We take decisions through members' meetings, with voting rights for all tenants. These are held every month (and sometimes more frequently) in our community 'hut'.

A number of smaller working groups implement the day to day management required, assisted by three part time paid workers. Individual houses have a shared living room and kitchen and their own level of communal living, though we all share communal gardens and an allotment on our three acre site.

Our houses are in an urban environment in close proximity to the railway. They are for four, six and ten bedroom houses and we also have eight one bedroom flats. With vacancies occuring fairly frequently we are always interested in applications from self-motivated people who are aware of the responsibilities and fun to be had from living co-operatively.

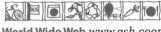

World Wide Web *www.ash.coop*

Ashram Community began in 1967, with the intention of developing committed urban communities, which would develop appropriate new forms of Christian community related to urban needs. This led to having inner-city Community Houses in the 1970's to 1990's, in seven cities. Now, it is concentrated in Sheffield.

There are three 2-person Community Houses and three Community Flats, plus two shop projects. The first of these, the Ashram Centre and New Roots Shop (wholefoods, fruit and veg, Traidcraft) was opened in 1987. The second, the Burngreave Ashram, was opened in 2001. It is a complex of shops and residences, with accommodation for six asylum seekers, a multi-faith chapel/library, a kitchen and cafe for community groups, weekly Free Meals, and other community services, all run by volunteers, members and residents.

The Community sustains its radical Christian base through regional Branches, half-yearly Weekends and half-yearly Community General Meetings, plus Inner City Retreats, Study and Research, Summer School, Holidays, and other occasions. The Community wrote and published a *Discovery Course in Radical Christianity* called *Journey*, and sponsors Radical Christianity conferences and Radical Christian Books. In 2009, it published its story and philosophy in *A Lifestyle of Sharing* (Ashram Press.) A Study and Research Group on Christian Intentional Community involves other Communities and invites all interested.

Ashram Community

Postal Address
178 Abbeyfield Road
Sheffield S4 7AY

Telephone
0114 243 6688

Electronic Mail
ashramcommunity
@hotmail.com

Over 18s
45

Under 18s
0

Year started
1967

Situation
urban

Ideological focus
radical Christian

Legal structure
registered charity

Open to new members?
yes

Charge visitors?
no

Work in lieu?
no

World Wide Web *http://www.ashram.org.uk*

Auchinleck Housing Co-op

Postal Address
20 Stanley Road
Edinburgh
EH6 4SG

Electronic Mail
auchinleckcooperative
@gmail.com

Auchinleck Housing Co-operative is a women's co-op in the Newhaven area, on the north side of Edinburgh. We are currently eight women – lesbian, bisexual and straight – ranging in age from 20s to 60s.

The house is a three-storey Victorian semi-detached house, with front and back gardens, two living rooms and spare bedrooms for guests. We have communal dinners cooked from organic veg boxes and produce from our garden.

Decisions are made at meetings which we hold once or twice a month, the aim is to share equal responsibility for cleaning, maintenance, accounts, gardening, admin etc. When we are looking for new members we will post here and on gumtree.

Over 18s
7

Under 18s
0

Year started
1981

Situation
urban

Legal structure
industrial and provident society

Open to new members?
yes

Charge visitors?
no

Work in lieu?
no

We live in a large country house in the rolling Devon hills. Accommodation is both rented and leasehold, in converted outbuildings and in the main house. On our seven acres of land we grow organic fruit and vegetables. We have a paddock,chickens, an orchard, a vineyard, a walled garden, a swimming pool, compost toilets and a reed-bed sewage system as well as a wind turbine, solar panels and a log boiler.

Together we run a low-key course centre and any excess income is used on community projects. We share responsibility for our home and the land on which we live and have a shared meal together in the evening.

We participate in the wider community, promoting awareness of everyone's impact on the environment through working closely with the local Climate Action group, hosting the village community composting scheme on our site, and holding occasional community open days.

Individuals earn incomes in the wider world in journalism, education, recycling, complementary health, alternative ceremonies and handyman work. We do not favour dogmatism, judgement or preaching, and aim to care for one another and enjoy life. We tolerate each others' differences and enjoy having visitors and volunteers. Please send an s.a.e. for more information. We are now offering bed and breakfast with www.airbnb.co.uk. Search under Morchard Bishop then 'Eco-break...'

Beech Hill Community

Postal Address
Morchard Bishop
Crediton
EX17 6RF

Telephone
01363 877228

Electronic Mail
beechhill@gmail.com

Over 18s
12

Under 18s
3

Year started
1983

Situation
rural

Ideological focus
ecological

Legal structure
company limited by guarantee

Open to new members?
yes

Charge visitors?
yes

Work in lieu?
yes

World Wide Web *http://www.beechhillcommunity.org.uk*

Birchwood Hall Community

Location
WR13 5EZ

Electronic Mail
info@birchwoodhall.org.uk

Over 18s
18

Under 18s
2

Year started
1970

Situation
rural

Ideological focus
none

Legal structure
co-operative

Open to new members?
yes

Charge visitors?
no

Work in lieu?
no

We live as a communal household to fulfil a variety of personal and political values. We do not try to be self-sufficient, though a number of us enjoy growing vegetables. We sympathise with many green and feminist principles, but we are a varied group. Key to our success is that we like each other!

The community is currently 14 adults and several children. We enjoy entertaining friends, relatives and other visitors, so the household can sometimes be quite busy!

We own the property as a group, but with no individual equity. We each pay a weekly income-related rent covering most household costs. We aim to keep Birchwood an affordable place for anyone to live.

Birchwood Hall, four miles from Malvern, consists of two large houses with eight acres of grounds, plus a residential centre called Anybodys Barn, run as a separate charity. Each member has a personal room, and we share a variety of communal spaces.

Most of us work outside the community and lead busy lives, so members need to be fairly self-reliant, though we are good at providing support in time of need. We eat our evening meal together every day and make decisions by consensus. But the community is not a "project" – it is a home for those who live here.

We are currently creating more living space and assessing how our two buildings will work together in the longer term, and we are also looking for new members, so this is a time of change for us. Please don't expect to join tomorrow; we need to get to know each other over time to ensure that your joining will work for everyone.

If you would like more information or to enquire about joining, send an email telling us something about yourself.

World Wide Web *http://www.birchwoodhall.org.uk*

Bowden House Community is a thriving intentional community which has been established since 2005 one mile from Totnes in rural Devon. We are a group of families and individuals enjoying learning to live consciously together and with our environment. We don't have any ideological or religious focus in common and accept the diversity of backgrounds and beliefs reflected in our members.

Our land includes an orchard, walled garden, large herb and vegetable gardens and two polytunnels, newly planted woodland, ornamental gardens and lawns. We also share facillities like a wood workshop, community centre, clay pizza oven, tractor, events/workshop spaces etc.

Some of the things which are important to us include: singing, music, arts and crafts; developing our communication skills with each other; collaborating on community projects and the day to day running of things: celebrating and sharing food together; sustainability, organic gardening, forest gardening, biodiversity; deepening our cennection with each other and the land we live on.

Most of the properties in the grounds are privately owned and lived in by individual/family members of the community. Currently there is a housing co-operative developing in the Manor House (pictured) which will include some more communal living space as well as new private accomodation. Please feel free to contact us to find out more about any aspect of our community.

Bowden House Community

Postal Address
Bowden House
Totnes
TQ9 7PW

Electronic Mail
info@bowdenhouse.co.uk

Over 18s
26

Under 18s
15

Year started
2005

Situation
rural

Ideological focus
"the alchemy of living together"

Legal structure
housing co-operative plus some private ownership

Open to new members?
yes

Charge visitors?
no

Work in lieu?
no

World Wide Web *http://www.bowdenhouse.co.uk*

Braziers Community

Founded in 1950, Braziers is a non-religious community and a college. The main house is Strawberry Hill Gothic in style and is set in 50 acres of unspoilt Oxfordshire countryside. Longer-term residents with a variety of backgrounds and interests live here and, in addition, there are usually three or four foreign students who come to improve their English and help run the house and grounds. We also have WWOOFers and HelpXers.

Braziers is broadly evolutionist in outlook and has a particular interest in group process and group communication. We have paying guests most weekends and are a popular venue for wedding parties, groups and courses such as yoga, meditation, Forest School Camps and the annual Wood Festival, Supernormal and Sacred Arts Camp.

We also run some of our own courses including beekeeping, organic gardening, spinning and community building. Visitors may either stay in the house or opt to camp in the meadows. There are 28 guest bedspaces in the house, but camping allows us to accommodate up to 1000 self catering.

Our cooking has a seasonal, local and organic emphasis, mainly vegetarian dishes are served. Many of the vegetables come from our own organic kitchen garden, our meat is reared on site and served occasionally. Our land management is sympathetic to nature with commitment to sustainable life.

The atmosphere at Braziers is informal, relaxed and supportive. If you would like to know more about Braziers, our courses and events or to find out about hiring Braziers as a venue, please visit our website.

Postal Address
Braziers Park
Ipsden
Wallingford
OX10 6AN

Electronic Mail
volunteers@braziers.org.uk

Over 18s
14

Under 18s
1

Year started
1950

Situation
rural

Ideological focus
evolutionist ecological

Legal structure
friendly society

Open to new members?
yes

Charge visitors?
yes

Work in lieu?
yes

World Wide Web *http://www.braziers.org.uk*

As stewards of this 80-acre farm, we try to live our lives working with rather than against nature: husbanding goats, ducks, chickens and bees for milk, eggs and honey; producing organic fruit and veg from polytunnels and large gardens. We coppice wood for fuel, bake bread, preserve produce, and use our own materials such as wood and willow for craftwork.

Accommodation is the traditionally built farmhouse and its outbuildings, electricity is supplied by wind, water and solar and we have a couple of green-design buildings. Communal activities include 3 to 5 meals per week (mostly vegetarian, but sometimes including meat), a weekly meeting and members contribute 18 hours per week of unpaid community work.

We run courses and occasional camps, and are able to host small gatherings and workshops. Visitors are welcome by prior arrangement. See our website or email for details on volunteering, short or long term, and on info weekends and courses. Languages spoken are English, Welsh, Dutch, French, German and Spanish. Smoking is restricted to private living spaces, and outside.

Brithdir Mawr

Postal Address
Ffordd Cilgwyn
Trefdraeth SA42 0QJ

Telephone
01239 820164

Electronic Mail
visit@brithdirmawr.co.uk

Over 18s
13

Under 18s
0

Year started
1994

Situation
rural

Ideological focus
ecological

Legal structure
company limited by guarantee and housing co-op

Open to new members?
yes

Charge visitors?
no

Work in lieu?
yes

World Wide Web *http://brithdirmawr.co.uk*

Canon Frome Court

Postal Address
Canon Frome
Ledbury HR8 2TD

Electronic Mail
membership@
canonfromecourt.org.uk

Over 18s
28

Under 18s
21

Year started
1978

Situation
rural

Ideological focus
organic farming, food and friends with widely green/ left values

Legal structure
industrial and provident society

Open to new members?
yes

Charge visitors?
no

Work in lieu?
yes

The main house and stable block contain 19 leasehold self-contained living spaces of varying sizes, housing some 28 adults (aged between 31 and late 60's) and 21 children. The community includes a meeting room for our weekly meetings (decision making is mostly by consensus); communal guest rooms; a dairy kitchen for making cheese, yoghurt and butter; a communal dining room for shared meals on Saturdays, holidays and other occasions and where we also host workshops (basket making, pilates, live music events etc); the gym which is a huge hall, for parties, ceilidhs and singing and dance workshops; and a shop for wholefoods and chocolate. There are communal workspaces for metal and woodwork.

Our mixed farm of 40 acres supports a variety of animals — dairy and beef cattle, goats, sheep, chickens, and bees. The large walled garden produces year-round veg from year round work, with some help from WWOOFers.

Then there is the front lawn for picnics, barbecues and the children's play area, a lake for boating and wildlife and even a swimming pool.

We have recently installed a PV array to produce electricity and have also installed a biomass heating system using wood from local woodland. Canon Fromers like to work, rest and play!

World Wide Web *http://www.canonfromecourt.org.uk*

The Cohousing Company received planning permission in June 2005 for the first CoFlats community. CoFlats is similar to Cohousing but it's just flats. Stroud Coflats has a shared car, an on-site 2KW wind turbine, super-insulation and re-uses an old chapel in the Town Centre.

There is a common house, two garden areas, 20 secure bicycle lockups, 14 flats and studios.

The related Cohousing Company built the first new-build cohousing community in the UK in Stroud (see Springhill Cohousing entry). And the 3rd Cohousing Community in Stroud. CoFlats Sladbrook.

The principles of Cohousing are that decisions are made by consensus, the site is pedestrianised, the common house is used for shared meals and is a communal extension to residents' private living rooms.

Cohousing is the future. Communal when we want it and privacy when we want it.

CoFlats Lansdown
•
CoFlats Sladbrook

Postal Address
Cohousing Company
16 Springhill Cohousing,
Uplands
Stroud GL5 1TN

Telephone
01453 766466

Electronic Mail
info@coflats.com

Over 18s
14

Year started
2006

Situation
urban

Ideological focus
cohousing

Legal structure
company limited by shares

Open to new members?
yes

Charge visitors?
no

Work in lieu?
no

World Wide Web *http://www.coflats.com*

Cohousing Bristol

Postal Address
Lower Knowle Farm
Berrow Walk, Bedminster
Bristol
BS3 5ES

Electronic Mail
jude.blodwen@
blueyonder.co.uk

Over 18s
11

Under 18s
0

Year started
2001

Situation
urban

Legal structure
company limited by
guarantee

Open to new members?
yes

Charge visitors?
no

Work in lieu?
no

CoHousing Bristol is a small cohousing project in South Bristol within easy reach of the city centre. In 2010 we bought a property consisting of a stone-built farmhouse and just under an acre of land. It was in need of extensive renovation, and we moved in in 2011 after working on it for a year.

We are currently in the process of creating a cohousing community on our site, providing socially, environmentally and financially sustainable housing and shared community facilities for our members and have recently applied for planning permission to build 9 housing units for sale to members.

CoHousing Bristol is a company limited by guarantee and was originally set up in 2001. The group bid for various properties or parcels of land unsuccessfully before acquiring our current site.

Our group currently lives onsite in the farmhouse.

CoHousing Bristol Ltd members are also directors of the company and need to be able to commit time and energy to developing the project over the next few years.

Corani is a small housing and land co-operative established in 1978 and based in Devon and Leicester. On the edge of the town of Crediton in Devon 6 residents live in a semi-detached Georgian house bought by Corani in 2013. In Leicester two residents live in a terraced Victorian house bought by Corani in 1996. Three other members, not currently housed by Corani, live elsewhere in Leicester.

The Crediton house has a large garden around it in which we grow as many fruits, vegetables and herbs as we can, whilst leaving enough space to play football with the dog. Chickens will be joining us soon and we have a homemade beehive with a successful colony that produces delicious honey. We aim to live as sustainably as we can in our current situation. The Leicester house has recently installed solar panels and the Crediton house have ongoing work making the house as insulated as possible.

The Corani members in each house share all communal living spaces. In Crediton we eat together every evening and have a casual cooking rota means that everyone cooks at least once a week. Decision making is essentially pragmatic: by consensus where all are concerned, otherwise with sensitive autonomy. The things that some or all of us like to do are: being outside, growing things, making things, carpentry, plumbing, playing music, dancing, climbing rocks and mountains, camping, bird watching, peer counselling, promoting sustainability, promoting devolved government. We don't currently have the capacity to take on new members, but may wish to do so in the future, so if you would like to learn more about Corani then please do get in touch.

Corani Housing and Land Co-op

Postal Address
*1 Taw Vale Terrace
Station Road
Crediton
EX17 3BU*

Electronic Mail
info@corani.org

Over 18s
11

Under 18s
0

Year started
1978

Situation
urban/ semi-urban

Ideological focus
co-operative/sharing

Legal structure
industrial and provident society

Open to new members?
yes

Charge visitors?
no

Work in lieu?
no

World Wide Web *http://www.corani.org*

Cordata Co-op

Location
M20 3EA

Electronic Mail
*mailcordatacoop
@gmail.com*

Over 18s
6

Under 18s
0

Year started
2013

Situation
urban

Legal structure
*industrial and provident
society*

Open to new members?
yes

Charge visitors?
no

Work in lieu?
no

Cordata Co-operative is the first of several new co-operative house projects that enable groups of people to live in a more sustainable way in large urban houses. Cordata co-operative is in Withington in south Manchester. The house is owned by a secondary co-operative and run by members of the co-operative house, who have complete control over who lives there; how the space is used; and what it looks like. This model also allows for a complete low energy refurbishment, so we have fitted solar panels, a complete insulation envelope, rainwater collection, and other energy reducing features.

Current members are a diverse group of people: musician, lecturer, chef, student, dance teacher, freelance film-maker. At summer 2015, after an intense year of finishing off the internal work on the house and developing our principles, we are now focusing on living together, and supporting other houses using the same model.

We are a registered co-operative and we meet about every month to make bigger decisions and develop our group. Some of our principles include a commitment to cooking and eating together, managing energy use, and being creative with a small amount of food growing space.

We occasionally have places available in the house and are happy to help other groups who are interested in something similar. Contact us by e-mail or look for our page on Facebook (The Cordata House). We are part of a small network of co-operative houses supported by the Co-operative Living Freehold Society.

World Wide Web *http://www.cordatacoop.org.uk*

Cornerstone is not so much a community as a collective of people who share the running of a housing co-op, but who have different political perspectives and focuses for their daily lives.

Cornerstone has two large Victorian houses in Chapeltown, a culturally diverse part of inner-city Leeds. Both houses need a lot of ongoing maintenance, and have large gardens front and back, which we variously hang out in, tend or leave wild, attracting wildlife and producing some food (herbs, fruit and veg).

One house has space for seven members, the other for eight, and there are sometimes short and long-term visitors increasing our numbers. Both houses have large cellars which are home to a wide range of projects – bikes, workshops, brewing, a garden nursery, a resource centre and Footprint Workers Co-operative (printers).

We have been able to support a variety of other co-operatives to grow and develop within Leeds. There is an emphasis on members being socially active, and are often involved in local and national campaigns on a diverse range of issues with emphasis on consensus and non-hierarchy.

We eat together, run the houses together, and make decisions together. Cornerstone is an active member of Radical Routes, the UK-wide secondary co-op promoting co-operation and working for radical social change.

Cornerstone Housing Co-op

Postal Address
16 Sholebroke Avenue
Chapeltown
Leeds LS7 3HB

Telephone
0113 262 9365

Electronic Mail
cornerstone@
cornerstonehousing.org.uk

Over 18s
16

Year started
1993

Situation
urban

Ideological focus
multiple/diverse

Legal structure
industrial and provident society

Open to new members?
yes

Charge visitors?
no

Work in lieu?
no

World Wide Web *http://www.cornerstonehousing.org.uk*

The Courtyards

W e are currently six households consisting of 10 adults and 6 children. Our home is situated on the outskirts of Bradford on Avon near Bath in a converted school building, which used to be a large manor house. We have around 8 acres of land, an orchard, plenty of room to grow some veg and some old mature trees. Other amenities include a large communal hall, outdoor swimming pool, tennis court and a sauna.

We also have solar panels to provide community electricity and a reed bed sewage system that treats all our waste.

Many of us have been living together since 1996. At the moment we get together one day a month to work and share meals. We have meetings when there is a need and there are regular events such as dancing and book and singing groups that often run from our communal hall.

At the time of writing the Courtyards Community has two building plots with planning permission for two semi-detached 3 or 4 bedroom houses. This may be of interest to people who would like to live in an established co-housing community but build their own home.

Location
BA15 2PB

Electronic Mail
*courtyardscommunity
@outlook.com*

Over 18s
10

Under 18s
6

Year started
1996

Situation
rural

Legal structure
company limited by guarantee

Open to new members?
yes

Charge visitors?
no

Work in lieu?
no

Coventry Peace House is in a multi-cultural area, 15 minutes walk from the city centre. The original six terraced houses have now been turned into two buildings which encompass living space and a cycle workshop (which is open to others) and a large community space. This is used by us and by the local community for various projects in the day and at night we use it as a night shelter for refused refugees.

Other projects come and go with the inspiration, hard work and enthusiasm of members and friends. There is a large back garden and a big warm kitchen with a wood burner so you can pretend you are in the country and still have access to the people and activities which cities provide. There is no television.

We are not affiliated to any religious group or political party but are a member of Radical Routes and have a commitment to radical social change. We like visitors and hold activity weekends on the first full weekend of every month. We welcome musicians, carpenters, artists, philosophers, poets, children, gardeners, builders and cyclists. We prefer members to work in part time employment so they have enough energy to work hard in the co-op and to change the world.

Coventry Peace House

Postal Address
311 Stoney Stanton Road
Coventry CV6 5DS

Telephone
024 7666 4616

Electronic Mail
info@
covpeacehouse.org.uk

Over 18s
7

Under 18s
0

Year started
1999

Situation
urban

Ideological focus
peace

Legal structure
industrial and provident society

Open to new members?
yes

Charge visitors?
no

Work in lieu?
yes

World Wide Web *http://www.covpeacehouse.org.uk*

Crabapple Community

Postal Address
Berrington Hall
Berrington
Shrewsbury SY5 6HA

Electronic Mail
crabapplecom
@hotmail.com

Over 18s
10

Under 18s
6

Year started
1975

Situation
rural

Ideological focus
ecological

Legal structure
company limited by guarantee

Open to new members?
yes

Charge visitors?
yes

Work in lieu?
no

Crabapple occupies a slightly eccentric Georgian rectory 5 miles south-east of Shrewsbury, with approx 20 acres of woodland, and growing areas, including a 2 acre walled fruit and vegetable garden, a community-supported market garden, several polytunnels, an orchard, a willow plantation, herb and flower gardens, plus two camping meadows.

We aim to live as sustainably as we can and to be self sufficient in produce for at least some of the year. We grow everything organically with a diversity of approaches. The house is heated in the winter with a log-boiler and central heating system (installed 2010). We cook on a wood-burning range which also provides our hot water, together with the solar thermal system (installed 2015). We also have a 4kW photovoltaic array (2012).

The general running of the community is organised through a flexible rota system and members contribute two days work each week e.g. gardening, preserving food, cleaning, house maintenance and renovation, wood processing, hedging, meadow mowing, organising events, admin/finance, etc... We are either self-employed or have part time jobs outside the community.

The community is constituted as a fully mutual housing co-op. You don't need capital to join – each tenant pays rent for a private room and access to shared facilities in the house, plus a weekly charge for housekeeping which covers food and other bills. We share a vegetarian/vegan meal (almost) every evening.

We aim to be part of the wider community through our CSA market garden, by using the house and grounds as a venue for groups and courses, and by hosting gatherings in our camping fields – including national environmental/peace campaign camps. Also, some of us are involved with local campaigning and cultural groups. We try to create a supportive environment for residents and visitors. We welcome WWOOFers on a regular basis – starting with an initial visit of 1 to 2 weeks.

Crescent Road Community was founded in 1978. At teh time of writing we are in the process of being evicted by our social housing landlord after living in the properties for 36 years. We are prepared to fight this and welcome your support with a campaign to save the community including a petition.

The Community consists of three houses which are interlinked on the ground floor. We are currently 20 adults and 3 children consisting of senior citizens, employed workers, and families.

We are close to London and have some lovely gardens and shared facilities including three kitchens, work shop rooms, TV room, laundry and meeting room. We grow some of our own vegetables and encourage communal meals and events. We pay our rent collectively to our housing association.

There is also a network of wider local community people with environmental interests linked to the houses in a social capacity.

We don't always have spaces but when we do we welcome applicants with social housing needs, including disabled people and single parents, some of our residents are key workers. Applicants are chosen via our equal opportunity allocations policy.

Crescent Road Community

Location
KT2 7RD

Electronic Mail
*crescentroadcommunity
@hotmail.co.uk*

Over 18s
20

Under 18s
3

Year started
1978

Situation
urban

Ideological focus
ecological

Legal structure
-

Open to new members?
no

Charge visitors?
yes

Work in lieu?
no

Darvell Community

Location
Robertsbridge
TN32 5DR

Electronic Mail
info@bruderhof.com

Over 18s
160

Under 18s
150

Year started
1920

Situation
rural

Ideological focus
Christian

Legal structure
registered charity

Open to new members?
yes

Charge visitors?
no

Work in lieu?
yes

The Darvell Community is located in the hills of East Sussex, about one hundred kilometres south of London, near the southern England coastline. The rolling hills that immediately surround Darvell include woods and hedge-lined fields, usually grazed by sheep and cows.

On our property you'll find brick apartment buildings and communal buildings including a dining hall, meeting room, kitchen, laundry, school, offices, and factory.

We are part of the Bruderhof movement. Founded in 1920 in Germany, the Bruderhof ("place of brothers" in German) has its roots in the Anabaptist tradition of Europe's Radical Reformation. We practice adult baptism. We are also pacifists and conscientious objectors. While we love our countries and countrymen, our faith transcends political and nationalistic affiliations. Our life together is founded on Jesus, the Christ and son of God. We are convinced that a life in church community is the greatest service we can offer humanity and the best way we can proclaim Christ. The Bruderhof movement is not a lifestyle choice. It is an answer to Jesus' insistent call to humankind as expressed in the Gospels, especially the Sermon on the Mount.

While we follow the communal traditions of the early church, we believe our way of life is a compelling answer to the problems of contemporary society, with its emphasis on wealth and self, and its resulting isolation, conflict, and inequality. Through community, we have experienced Christ's transforming love. He makes the impossible possible: for ordinary and flawed men and women to live together in forgiveness and mutual trust, as brothers and sisters. It is his Spirit that calls Bruderhof members to a life of love where work, worship, mission, education, and family life are brought together into a single whole.

World Wide Web *http://www.bruderhof.com*

Dol-llys Housing Ltd was formed in 1992 by 6 families to purchase Dol-llys Hall; originally a regency country house but then empty and owned by Powys County Council. It was legally established as a housing co-operative as this was the most appropriate way to make a shared purchase and create affordable homes.

The house is divided into seven private, self contained flats of varying size, one of which is rented. We also have some communal rooms in the house and share all the outdoor space. New members buy into the co-operative through purchasing loan stock giving them a ⅙th ownership of the entire property and grounds.

Daily life at Dol-Llys is more in line with co-housing. A key difference is that we are not an "intentional community" in the general ideological sense. We have different outlooks and lifetyles; our focus is mainly practical and is centred on sharing and caring for communal space, green space and some material resources. We share workloads equitably and this means we can all enjoy and benefit from sharing the house and gardens and some resources.

By meeting, working co-operatively and eating together each month we are able to build friendly neighbourly relationships. If you are interested in living at Dol-llys, please contact the Secretary via the Dol-llys website or by email for the latest information on the availability of shares.

Dol-llys Hall

Postal Address
Dol llys Hall
Llanidloes
SY18 6JB

Electronic Mail
info@dol-llys.co.uk

Over 18s
12

Under 18s
5

Year started
1992

Situation
semi-rural

Ideological focus
environmentally aware

Legal structure
industrial and provident society

Open to new members?
yes

Charge visitors?
no

Work in lieu?
no

World Wide Web *http://www.dol-llys.co.uk*

Earth Heart

Location
DE6 1NS

Electronic Mail
earth.heart
@hotmail.co.uk

Over 18s
14

Under 18s
4

Year started
1997

Situation
rural

Ideological focus
ecological, natural parenting, home-based education

Legal structure
industrial and provident society

Open to new members?
yes

Charge visitors?
yes

Work in lieu?
no

Earth Heart Housing Co-op is a co-housing community in a very quiet and beautiful part of rural Derbyshire close to the Peak District. We own the freehold of the Grade II listed converted farmhouse and barns. The east wing of the barns is partially converted to create a communal hall for meetings and gatherings, as well as workshop space and storage. We are as ecological as we can manage/afford, having a communal woodpellet boiler for heating, a reed bed waste-water treatment system and using a green electricity company. The surrounding 21 acres of organic land is managed primarily for nature conservation. There is a large parkland running down to Henmore Brook with a moat and other small pastures (grazed with a local organic farmer's sheep and cows); a secluded woodland with a tree circle; a community orchard and allotments with vegetables, fruit and herbs; a willow labyrinth and dome; a composting toilet and solar shower dome. Members own 900+ year leases on the eight individual homes and each home has private use of a small garden. We aim for a diverse group of people of a variety of ages, including singles, couples and families with children, with home-owning members as well as tenants and non-member lodgers. Most are employed off site but some work from home. We have the advantage of being able to enjoy our independent lives whilst also living within a mutually supportive and sociable community. We have community work days and business meetings once a month and occasional 'sharing' meetings. Important decisions are taken by consensus and general management is carried out by land, maintenance, finance and admin teams. We understand that nothing gets done unless we all contribute so we have a minimum co-op work requirement for every resident with an expectation of everyone doing a fair share. We expect people to participate regularly in co-op meetings but they are not compulsory. We are not open to the public but offer guided walks and workshops for groups of 6 people or more. We also host and run various camps during the spring and summer and are happy to consider hosting new groups for camps. Opportunities arise from time to time to buy, rent or lodge here. If you are interested in visiting with a view to going on our waiting list, do email us for further details.

Please explore our website if you're interested in what we're up to. There are 14 people in our co-op which is more of a co-housing project than a community in the more intentional intimacy sense of the word.

Being a co-op means we all take decisions on the running of the project together, all pay rent and all join in a certain amount of admin and renovation work.

The co-op has seven acres including orchards, kitchen garden, woodland, lounging lawns and a wetland designed by J Abraham that manages all of our sewage and waste water.

There are three buildings made of up three flats, a small house, a 6-person shared house set-up and lots of large communal rooms. We are focused on renovation more than land management for the foreseeable future (2015-2019).

We are not a food/land based project at present, so it isn't appropriate to take WWOOFers. We do sometimes have work weeks on renovation and maintenance of the buildings though; please e-mail us with Volunteer in the subject for more information.

We see our focus as being diverse but involving permaculture and a lot of very hard graft!

Earthworm Housing Co-op

Postal Address
Wheatstone House
High St, Leintwardine
Craven Arms SY7 0LH

Telephone
01547 540461

Electronic Mail
earthwormcooperative
@yahoo.co.uk

Over 18s
9

Under 18s
1

Year started
1989

Situation
in a village

Ideological focus
very hard graft

Legal structure
ind & prov society

Open to new members?
yes

Charge visitors?
yes

Work in lieu?
no

World Wide Web *http://www.earthwormhousingcooperative.org.uk/*

Edinburgh Student Housing Co-op

Postal Address
28 & 34 Wright's Houses
Edinburgh
EH10 4HR

Electronic Mail
edinburghstudenthousingcoop
@gmail.com

Over 18s
106

Under 18s
0

Year started
2014

Situation
urban

Legal structure
industrial and provident Society

Open to new members?
yes

Charge visitors?
no

Work in lieu?
no

Edinburgh Student Housing Co-operative is a 106 member fully mutual co-operative, entirely self-managed by its members. Student housing co-operatives are a new phenomenon in Britain, first starting in 2014, with ESHC currently the largest.

Alongside being a unique experiment in communal living, the co-operative is also the city's cheapest student housing provider by a sizeable margin.

The co-operative uses a participatory, consensus based model, with all major decisions being made by general meeting. ESHC also has two large communal basement spaces, regularly playing host to bands, film nights, political discussions, community groups, theatre groups and parties. The co-operative has a growing radical library, which we plan to make available to non-members as well.

From plumbing to feminism, the co-operative is also a great place to learn new skills, and explore new ideas. As part of being self-managed, members are able to take part in training workshops in facilitation skills, conflict mediation, basic accounting, first aid, and more.

Applications for membership are open each spring to students from any of the city's universities or colleges. Applications are extremely competitive, so do get in touch for more information before applying.

ESHC is a member of Students for Cooperation, a national federation of student co-operatives through which it works to set up new co-ops. If you're in the city then do pop by for a cup of tea and a tour.

World Wide Web *https://edinburghcoop.wordpress.com*

Erraid is a small Hebridean island in Scotland, in view of Iona. The island is one square mile in size and our small community lives and works on the land.

We live in old light house keepers' cottages, which we share with our guests. Life on Erraid seems pretty much like it must have been in the 1870s when the houses were established. We work in the gardens, heat the cottages and our water with woodburning stoves, bathe in peat water, drink rain water, use outdoor composting toilets and live a life very close to the elements. What we are doing on a day to day basis is often determined by the sea, the tides, the moon and the wind.

One of our main purposes on the island is to hold guests in the island's ancient energy and allow them to experience and explore its magnificent landscape and wildlife, our unique lifestyle and community life. Guests come throughout the year for a week or even months to live with us and join in our activities: cooking, chopping wood, working in the gardens, helping with the animals, making candles, meditating and singing sacred songs in our beautiful sanctuary and celebrating the turning of the seasons in our Celtic Festival weeks. If you would like further information, please feel free to contact us!

Isle of Erraid Community

Postal Address
Findhorn Foundation
Isle of Erraid
Fionnphort
Isle of Mull PA66 6BN

Telephone
01681 700384

Electronic Mail
erraid@live.co.uk

Over 18s
4

Under 18s
2

Year started
1977

Situation
rural inshore island

Ideological focus
sustainable-spiritual

Legal structure
registered charity

Open to new members?
yes

Charge visitors?
yes

Work in lieu?
no

World Wide Web *http://www.erraid.com*

Fireside Housing Co-op

Postal Address
61 Melrose Road
Sheffield
S3 9DN

Electronic Mail
fireside@
blueyonder.co.uk

Over 18s
9

Under 18s
2

Year started
1996

Situation
urban

Ideological focus
cheap but high quality living

Legal structure
industrial and provident society

Open to new members?
yes

Charge visitors?
no

Work in lieu?
no

Fireside has a row of four mid-terrace Victorian houses in Burngreave in Sheffield. We've knocked our four long and skinny gardens into one, so there's plenty of room for us to play, grow organic veg, have bonfires and parties. The gardens back onto a Victorian cemetery so there's lots of green space and wildlife around even though we're in an inner-city area. There's also an adventure playground at the end of the road.

The age range of the nine adults and two teenagers living here is evenly staggered from teens to 50s. We live mostly as four separate households, but we have knocked connecting doors between numbers 55 and 57 and numbers 59 and 61 now have a shared kitchen area.

We eat communally on a fairly regular basis, particularly when having a workday on the houses or gardens. We're coming to the end of a big building project which demolished our damp, cramped kitchens and created a highly insulated 2-storey extension across the backs of 55-59. Exciting, and expensive!

Burngreave is a quite deprived inner-city area but very multicultural and vibrant. Many of the co-op members are involved with local community groups.

Forgebank is an eco cohousing development consisting of 35 leasehold homes, shared buildings and riverside woodland habitat. The site is just outside Lancaster on the outskirts of the village of Halton and offers stunning views of the river Lune.

We aspire to be a cutting edge example of sustainable 'eco' design, for both living and working, with close links to the local community. The homes have achieved both Passivhaus and Code for Sustainable Homes level 6 certifications, and we benefit from many eco technologies such as a biomass boiler, solar PV and hydroelectricity. The project was planned and designed by the residents with architects Eco Arc and local building firm Whittles Construction.

Residents, who are members of Lancaster Cohousing Ltd, actively participate in the day to day running of the community. Discussions are democratic and consensual. While we do have community agreements and policies, our ambition is to rely on trust, respect, friendship and understanding rather than rules and regulations.

Our Common House contains a communal kitchen and dining room where we cook vegan and vegetarian meals for each other several times a week. There are communal food stores, play areas, guest rooms, a bike shed and laundry. At the time of writing there are 3 homes for sale and 1 for rent. For more info and up-to-date news see our website.

Forgebank

Postal Address
9 Forgebank Walk, Halton
Lancaster LA2 6FD

Telephone
07825 610342

Electronic Mail
info@
lancastercohousing.org.uk

Over 18s
61

Under 18s
15

Year started
2012

Situation
urban/rural edge

Ideological focus
Sustainable living

Legal structure
company limited by guarantee

Open to new members?
yes

Charge visitors?
no

Work in lieu?
no

World Wide Web *http://www.lancastercohousing.org.uk*

Guiseppe Conlon House

Postal Address
49 Mattison Road
London
N4 1BG

Electronic Mail
londoncatholicworker
@yahoo.co.uk

Over 18s
5

Under 18s
0

Year started
2010

Situation
urban

Ideological focus
ecumenical Catholic
anarchist pacifist

Legal structure
unincorporated

Open to new members?
yes

Charge visitors?
no

Work in lieu?
yes

We are a community of the radical Christian "Catholic Worker" movement. The Catholic Worker is an ecumenical, pacifist, and anarchist movement founded by Dorothy Day and Peter Maurin in New York in 1933.

As a community we are dedicated to living simply, in solidarity with those who are marginalised by society and in resistance to violence and injustice.

The London Catholic Worker was brought together by the Jubilee Ploughshares 2000 disarmament action, in response to the need for a Catholic Worker community of hospitality and resistance in the world's second imperial city. In June 2010 the London Catholic Worker opened Guiseppe Conlon House. At Guiseppe Conlon House we provide hospitality for destitute refugees and asylum seekers. We have a community meal every evening and other activities such as prayer, bible study and "round table discussions" which are open to all living in the house as well as friends, volunteers and visitors. We also run the Urban Table soup kitchen in Hackney every other Sunday.

As part of our work of resistance we organise vigils and are involved in campaigns against war, arms trade, drones, and in solidarity with migrants and refugees. We take as our manifesto the Gospels, the lives of the saints, especially our Catholic Worker founders Dorothy Day and Peter Maurin, and the Catholic Worker "Aims and Means"*. Our aim is "to build a new society in the shell of the old", "a society where it is easier to be good", bringing about a non-violent revolution by changing the world one heart at a time.

*www.catholicworker.org/cw-aims-and-means.html

We live in a custom-built community house sharing a belief in co-operation, negotiation and understanding, to arrange how we live together. The core values of our Housing Association home are that of respect, self-help, mutual support, and participation.

We currently have a very vibrant mix of people, skills and cultures from around the world. Over the years our roof has sheltered many fascinating people.

We have seen:

the development of ethical livelihoods...
www.zaytoun.org (Palestinian olive oil)
www.wholewoods.co.uk (Sustainable woodland skills and events)

the study of a variety of subjects...
from anthropology to town planning

and strong musical influences...
from British folk to flamenco.

Our garden has been supported via funding from BTCV's People's Places award and is somewhat of an oasis in the big smoke. House historian Mr Robert Bell has been here from the start and is well known for his guided tours.

Hargrave Road Community

Location
N19 5SJ

Telephone
020 7263 5094

Electronic Mail
*hargrave.community
@gmail.com*

Over 18s
12

Under 18s
0

Year started
1987

Situation
urban

Ideological focus
ecological/care

Legal structure
-

Open to new members?
no

Charge visitors?
no

Work in lieu?
no

Heartwood Community

Postal Address
*Blaen Y Wern,
Llangyndeyrn
Llangyndeyrn
Kidwelly SA17 5ES*

Electronic Mail
*hippiesontour
@yahoo.com*

Over 18s
8

Under 18s
4

Year started
1997

Situation
rural

Ideological focus
eco-permaculture

Legal structure
company limited by guarantee

Open to new members?
yes

Charge visitors?
yes

Work in lieu?
yes

Heartwood is an old dairy farm with 35 acres of land: woods, pasture, wetland, streams, orchards and gardens. We have a pony that pulls a cart and helps with woodland management. There are two goats providing milk, four hens, twelve ducks and four cats.

In the main house we share facilities and enjoy five vegetarian communal meals a week. Some of our members raise and eat their own animals (pigs and ducks). Our practice of permaculture and sustainability includes maintaining sustainable relationships with each other as well as with the land we live on. We use Non-Violent Communication and consensus decision making and this forms the basis of our community.

We are often looking for short term volunteers to help with vegetable gardening, landscaping a garden, maintenance and diy. We are open to visitors on a WWOOF basis (bed and board in exchange for 4 to 6 hours work a day). We don't take WWOOFers over Christmas and New Year. Please note that although we will try to work alongside you we may not always be able to and you will spend some of your stay working alone. Please let us know of any additional needs or medication you are taking.

Franciscan brothers first arrived here in 1921 to establish a home of refuge and rehabilitation for the large number of displaced men who were then tramping the roads of rural England. At the Friary they found a welcome as brothers, the restoration of their dignity through shared work, and the opportunity of rehabilitation and training. From this small beginning has grown the Society of St Francis, an Anglican order of men and women inspired by the example of Francis of Assisi; SSF now has communities of brothers and sisters, and many lay or 'tertiary' members, throughout the world.

Today at Hilfield Friary there continue to live the Franciscan brothers of SSF, but they are now joined by other men and women – young and old, married and single – who together constitute the Hilfield Friary Community. This Community shares in a rhythm of daily prayer, helps to look after the Friary land and buildings, and offers hospitality to guests and visitors. People of all backgrounds are welcome here – Christians, those of other faiths and of none – for rest, retreat, and renewal of life. The emergency provision for 'wayfarers' ended in 2004, but the Friary still provides a place of acceptance and supported living for those who are in particular need.

Following the example of Francis of Assisi there is a particular emphasis on living simply, generously and joyfully on God's earth. The land and the animals it supports are cared for and provide food for the community. There is a common table around which the Community and its guests share meals, and yet there is also time and space to be quiet and alone. The Friary is not just a beautiful, peaceful oasis; the Community has a concern for promoting justice and reconciliation in a troubled world, and for proclaiming a wise ecology in the face of our culture's environmental foolishness.

At the heart of the Friary lies the Chapel where the Community comes together for prayer four times a day. Celebrating the Eucharist and praying the scriptures in the Daily Office, as well as the times of silent meditation, bring us back to the source and goal of all creation, renew us in the life of Jesus Christ, and unite us with our brothers and sisters throughout the world.

Hilfield Friary

Postal Address
The Friary, Hilfield
Dorchester DT2 7BE

Telephone
01300 341345

Electronic Mail
hilfieldssf
@franciscans.org.uk

Over 18s
20

Under 18s
3

Year started
1921

Situation
rural

Ideological focus
christian (anglican)

Legal structure
registered charity (part of the Society of St Francis)

Open to new members?
yes

Charge visitors?
no

Work in lieu?
no

World Wide Web *http://hilfieldfriary.org.uk*

Hoathly Hill Community

Hoathly Hill is on the border of East and West Sussex, set in the beautiful High Weald, between the two villages of West Hoathly and Sharpthorne. There are currently about 70 people of all ages living at Hoathly Hill in 27 living units on about 25 acres of land, with vegetable, fruit and herb gardens, a square lawn with formal beds, a playing field, allotments and community buildings used for a kindergarten, sculpture and pottery and community events.

Location
RH19 4SJ

Electronic Mail
info@hoathlyhilltrust.org.uk

Over 18s
55

Under 18s
15

Year started
1972

Situation
rural on edge of village

Ideological focus
principles of Rudolf Steiner with strong interest in sustainability

Legal structure
company limited by guarantee

Open to new members?
yes

Charge visitors?
no

Work in lieu?
no

There are weekly community meetings, monthly work days, weekly Saturday cafés and celebration of the festivals of the year. Hoathly Hill Community was founded over 40 years ago by a group of people with a vision for community living supportive of home life and initiative taking. Many were committed to the philosophy of Rudolf Steiner, an Austrian thinker who founded Steiner Waldorf schools, biodynamic agriculture, anthroposophical medicine and much more.

The community has a membership process, in which people interested in living at Hoathly Hill get to know community members and participate in community events. There are no restrictions on membership or selection criteria. The main house, the outbuildings and the land were bought at auction in the 1970s and there was a joint mortgage until the 80s, when a 'restructuring' took place and most of the living units were sold as leases to individual leaseholders. The freeholder is Hoathly Hill Association Ltd, a housing association for all leaseholders. Some of the units and most of the land is currently under the stewardship of Hoathly Hill Trust. Hoathly Hill Trust is a charitable organisation facilitating and supporting community, environmental educational projects, such as Hoathly Hill Sculpture Studio, Hoathly Hill Forest Garden, The Herb Garden, The Bee Garden, Hoathly Hill Community Supported Agriculture, Pericles Theatre Company and The Elderly Project. We also have a community biomass boiler for our heating and hot water, run by Hoathly Hill Renewable Energy.

World Wide Web *http://www.hoathlyhilltrust.org.uk/*

The Hockerton Housing Project (HHP) is the UK's first earth sheltered, self-sufficient ecological housing development. The residents of the five houses generate their own clean energy, harvest their own water and recycle waste materials causing minimal pollution or carbon dioxide emissions. The houses are amongst the most energy efficient, purpose-built dwellings in Europe. The houses are the focus of a holistic way of living, which combines the production of organic foods, low intensity fish farming, promotion of wildlife, and the planting of thousands of trees.

The project was conceived in the early 1990's. It took two years to complete the planning agreement with the local authority and a further two years to build the homes and facilities.

Over the years the project has established itself as an exemplar of sustainable development. As a result of this, it has developed a range of services through the creation of a small on-site business. This workers' co-operative provides a level of employment for its members, whilst promoting sustainable development. Its activities include running guided tours, workshops, talks, consultancy and, soon to be launched, a match-making service.

Although each family has their own home, the community share food growing, site maintenance, managing the facilities and a common sustainable business.

Hockerton Housing Project

Postal Address
*The Watershed
Gables Drive, Hockerton
Southwell NG25 0QU*

Telephone
01636 816902

Electronic Mail
*contact@
hockertonhousingproject.org.uk*

Over 18s
11

Under 18s
9

Year started
1995

Situation
rural

Ideological focus
none

Legal structure
co ltd by guarantee

Open to new members?
yes

Charge visitors?
yes

Work in lieu?
no

World Wide Web *http://www.hockertonhousingproject.org.uk/*

Holy Rood House

Postal Address
*10 Sowerby Road
Sowerby, Thirsk
Y07 1HX*

Electronic Mail
*enquiries@
holyroodhouse.org.uk*

Over 18s
30

Under 18s
0

Year started
1993

Situation
rural/ market town

Ideological focus
*Christian; radical,
inclusive and open*

Legal structure
*company limited by
guarantee*

Open to new members?
yes

Charge visitors?
yes

Work in lieu?
no

A place of peace and tranquillity, overlooking the Hambledon Hills, the Centre for Health and Pastoral Care offers therapeutic and safe space for people of all ages. Discovering acceptance and a relaxed environment, guests find empowerment to work towards their own health and well being, with professional support from counsellors, psychotherapists, masseurs and creative arts therapists. The friendship and care of staff and the residential community, excellent home cooking, gardens and animals, laughter and sharing, create a sense of belonging, and a few days or a couple of weeks becomes an important oasis in life for many people.

The gentle Christian ethos of this open, radical community offers a space for guests to develop their own journey in a way that is right for them. Celebrating spiritual diversity, the community reflects theologically through research, accredited modular work and conferences arranged through The Centre for The Study of Theology and Health, an offshoot of Holy Rood House. Whatever draws you to Holy Rood House, as an individual or as a group, you will be sure to find it a special place, and we can be sure that our lives will be enriched by your visit.

World Wide Web *http://www.holyroodhouse.org.uk*

Islington Park Street Community

We are a community of individuals aged between 18 and 79. Our cultures and occupations are mixed and we share a large, communal house in Islington, near to the Highbury Corner end of Upper Street. We operate on a social housing policy which encourages those on low-income and in housing need to apply as future residents. We cook for each other and share house jobs. Big decisions are made by monthly meetings, small ones by scraps of paper on the notice board (the nerve centre.)

The house is a happy environment with lots of music, conversation, scrabble and summer nights on the balcony. The community has a lot to offer including great location, excellent transport links, wireless internet, a film projector for that cinema feel, two gardens (one of which has a listed fig tree) and two lovely terraces.

Some of our residents have been living here for almost 35 years. We feel very lucky to have such a warm, fun and supportive community right in the heart of London. We are involved in local community projects and some of our residents are involved in global/social justice campaigns. We aim to be more eco-friendly than at present, so any advice/auditing services would be appreciated. We are keen to make links with other communities like ours and to learn more about co-op living projects. We do not encourage visits due to the extremely high number of requests we get, but please do contact us if you have any questions about the way we live.

At the time of writing Islington Park Street Community is under threat of eviction. Check out the latest situation at our website.

Postal Address
38-44 Islington Park Street
Islington
London
N1 1PX

Electronic Mail
44figtree@gmail.com

Over 18s
18

Under 18s
0

Year started
1976

Situation
urban

Ideological focus
community

Legal structure
unincorporated

Open to new members?
yes

Charge visitors?
no

Work in lieu?
no

World Wide Web *http://www.islingtonparkstreet.org/*

Keveral Farm Community

Postal Address
Keveral Farm
Looe
PL13 1PA

Electronic Mail
keveralfarm
@yahoo.co.uk

Over 18s
11

Under 18s
0

Year started
1973

Situation
rural

Legal structure
housing co-op and worker's co-op

Open to new members?
yes

Charge visitors?
yes

Work in lieu?
yes

Keveral Farm has been a community since 1973. We live in a farmhouse, a barn conversion, an extended static caravan, and three other static caravans. These, together with our farm buildings, are owned and managed by our housing co-op, One Community. Members should attend monthly community meetings, and do two hours voluntary work per week maintaining and improving the house, buildings and land.

The 25 acres of farmland consists of veg plots, polytunnels, soft fruit, orchard, woodland, pasture and camping, and has been certified organic by the Soil Association for more than 30 years.

Our worker's co-op, Keveral Farmers, oversees the management of the land. Most members rent areas of the land or buildings to pursue their own projects or commercial activities, which include vegetables, micro-salads, soft fruit, apple juice and cider, woodland management and firewood, and managing a campsite.

We have done weekly veg box deliveries to local people since 1997. We run a two-week Permaculture Design Course every summer. This is held in our Visitor's Barn, which is also available for events and group visits. We are looking to expand our range of courses, which may include dry stone-walling and seed-saving. We accept WWOOFers and working visitors by arrangement. Further information on Keveral Farm is available on our website.

World Wide Web *http://www.keveral.org*

Landmatters is a rural permaculture co-operative in South Devon with a focus on low impact, nature connection and education. We live on 42 acres of pasture and semi-natural ancient woodland, with some naturally regenerating scrub and ancient hedgerows. The land is stewarded by 10 adults and 7 children living in low-impact structures, mostly benders and yurts, and is totally off-grid.

We grow some food (hope to grow more!), keep horses, hens and ducks, manage the woodlands, work communally, run educational events, car share, and use consensus decision-making and Way of Council, with the aim of creating a thriving, ecological community.

We are a Permaculture Association LAND demonstration site and a member of the WWOOF network. Visitor accommodation is usually camping with use of the communal kitchen. We celebrated our tenth anniversary in May 2013, and occasionally have spaces for new members to join us. For more info check out our website.

Landmatters Permaculture Community

Location
TQ9 7DL

Telephone
01803 712718

Electronic Mail
*landmatters
@googlemail.com*

Over 18s
9

Under 18s
7

Year started
2003

Situation
rural

Ideological focus
permaculture and more

Legal structure
*industrial and provident
society*

Open to new members?
no

Charge visitors?
no

Work in lieu?
yes

World Wide Web *http://www.landmatters.org.uk*

Laurieston Hall

This co-operative of around 20 adults is now embarking on its fifth decade. We live in and around a huge Edwardian house, with its walled garden, stables and cottages, surrounded by 135 acres of beautiful woods, pastures and marshland which stretch to a loch in the north. Trees we planted are now being coppiced. Living spaces use wood for heating and cooking. A hydro supplies much of our electricity.

Issues that affect everybody come to a weekly co-op meeting in which decisions are made by consensus. Co-operation is our common ideology; and we are generally better at dealing with tomorrow than next year; are supportive of each other as individuals as well as co-op members... and we try to have a good time!

From Easter to October we run a programme of events (music, self-help, creative, gay, etc.), called The People Centre. We grow as much fruit and vegetables as we can, keep cows, pigs, hens and bees, and do most of our own maintenance.

There are several ways of visiting us. You can book on a People Centre event or you can come on a Maintenance Week, (there are only three per year, so book early to avoid disappointment!).

Information about us and booking can be done via our annual newsletter. You can write to us requesting a paper copy or go to the link below to download the latest edition.

Postal Address
Laurieston
Castle Douglas
DG7 2NB

Electronic Mail
enquirylh@gmail.com

Over 18s
18

Under 18s
0

Year started
1972

Situation
rural

Ideological focus
co-operative

Legal structure
fully mutual co-op,
under I&PS rules

Open to new members?
yes

Charge visitors?
yes

Work in lieu?
no

World Wide Web *http://www.lauriestonhall.org.uk*

We are a small community of Christians based in a socio-economically deprived but culturally rich area of Birmingham. Part of the Lee Abbey Movement, our aim is to 'communicate Christ through relationships'.

Our core values are represented by the acronym HOPE: Hospitality, Openness, Prayer and Engagement.

We work closely with local churches, and seek to deepen our own faith as we also look to share the love of Jesus with those around us.

Lee Abbey Aston Small Missional Community

Location
B6 5ND

Electronic Mail
*leeabbeyaston
@yahoo.co.uk*

Over 18s
5

Under 18s
0

Year started
1988

Situation
urban

Ideological focus
Christian

Legal structure
registered charity

Open to new members?
yes

Charge visitors?
no

Work in lieu?
no

World Wide Web *http://leeabbey.org.uk/smc/*

Lifespan Community Collective

Location
S36 4JG

Electronic Mail
*lifespancommunitycollective
@yahoo.co.uk*

Over 18s
20

Under 18s
7

Year started
1978

Situation
rural

Ideological focus
ecological

Legal structure
*industrial and provident
society*

Open to new members?
yes

Charge visitors?
yes

Work in lieu?
yes

Lifespan Community Collective (aka Townhead Collective) is made up of around 20 adults, seven kids, four dogs and several chickens. We have 19 old railway cottages with 3 acres of land in rural Yorkshire.

The Community has been formed by a collection of environmental protesters, travellers and locals. We try to live sustainably with as little impact on the environment as possible. We are into growing our own organic fruit and veg from two large communal gardens containing polytunnels and greenhouses. We also have a medicinal/kitchen herb garden and tree nursery.

One of our defining features and strengths is that we produce all of our own electricity from solar and wind. We aim to have hydro-power at some point in the future! We also compost all of our own waste.

We all have our own personal spaces as well as communal areas comprising a living room, kitchen, pool room, office with internet access, a learning space, music room, workshops and kids' play-room/spaces.

A down-to-earth vibe and positive initiative is encouraged. In the recent past, we have been the proud winners of the 'Inter-community Volleyball Golden Bum Award'!

Visitors' space is available and extra helping hands are always appreciated. We now hold monthly work weekends.

World Wide Web *http://www.lifespancommunity.co.uk*

Lilac means Low Impact Living Affordable Community. We are an affordable, urban co-housing development in Leeds, West Yorkshire and have a unique shared ownership model which is the first of its kind in the world.

Our community consists of 20 private strawbale and timber eco-homes of different sizes, grouped around our shared common house and pond. Lilac is home to 35 adult members and 12 children, three dogs, three cats and a lot of frogs. Our site is designed using co-housing principles with shared facilities in the middle such as our common house with its dining room for communal meals, parlour for films, games and meetings, and guest rooms. We also have a shared workshop, launderette, a large play area, and lots of shared green space, allotments and gardens.

Our legal structure is a Mutual Home Ownership Society (MHOS) which is an equity based leaseholder scheme. The cost of the project is divided into equity shares which are allocated to members based on the size of their property and their income. The member buys their allocation of shares either on a monthly basis, in which case their payments are set at 35% of their net income, or in full on moving in. Members can take their equity with them on leaving, and the value of the equity shares is linked to average national earnings, ensuring the project remains affordable from one generation of residents to the next.

Our project is currently fully occupied and we have a small waiting list but we are committed to sharing our learning and model with other groups, and run regular study days and tours. Please see our website for details.

LILAC

Location
LS5 3AG

Telephone
07890 809143

Electronic Mail
info@lilac.coop

Over 18s
25

Under 18s
6

Year started
2008

Situation
urban

Ideological focus
various

Legal structure
industrial and provident society

Open to new members?
yes

Charge visitors?
no

Work in lieu?
no

World Wide Web *http://www.lilac.coop*

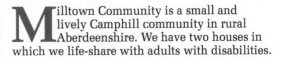

Milltown Community

Postal Address
Milltown
Arbuthnott
Laurencekirk
AB30 1PB

Electronic Mail
milltownoffice
@btconnect.com

Milltown Community is a small and lively Camphill community in rural Aberdeenshire. We have two houses in which we life-share with adults with disabilities.

We are a mix of co-workers who have been here for some time, employed co-workers who live locally and young volunteers who come for a year. We have a Day Workshop which is for adults with disabilities from the local area to come in to work on a daily basis. The Day Workshop runs a small plant nursery and a shop that sells our woodwork and craft products. It has a Tools for Self-Reliance enterprise that sends kits of refurbished tools to artisans and schools in Malawi.

We have beautiful gardens and a smallholding for vegetables, willows, sheep and hens. To find out more have a look at our website.

Over 18s
15

Under 18s
2

Year started
1990

Situation
rural

Ideological focus
A Camphill community

Legal structure
registered charity

Open to new members?
yes

Charge visitors?
no

Work in lieu?
yes

World Wide Web *http://www.milltowncommunity.org.uk*

W e are a small community living in a beautiful walled garden and orchard set around a medieval tower in sunny Fife. We grow all our own fresh produce, manage our woods for fuel and wildlife and look after the walls and the tower.

We are an environmental charity and offer opportunities for people to learn about organic gardening and low-impact, sustainable, communal living. We have a programme of events and courses and we host WWOOFers who volunteer We share food and eat together. We like to garden, play music, make stuff and generally have fun. For more information or an up-to-date course programme please write enclosing a stamped addressed envelope or email us.

Monimail Tower Project

Postal Address
Monimail
By Letham
Cupar
KY15 7RJ

Electronic Mail
monimailtower
@gmail.com

Over 18s
7

Under 18s
0

Year started
1984

Situation
rural

Ideological focus
ecological/sustainable

Legal structure
registered charity

Open to new members?
yes

Charge visitors?
yes

Work in lieu?
no

World Wide Web *http://www.monimail.org*

Monkton Wyld Court

Postal Address
Monkton Wyld Court
Elsdon's Lane
Bridport
DT6 6DQ

Electronic Mail
volunteer@
monktonwyldcourt.org

Over 18s
8

Under 18s
2

Year started
1982

Situation
rural

Ideological focus
education, sustainability

Legal structure
registered charity

Open to new members?
yes

Charge visitors?
yes

Work in lieu?
yes

Monkton Wyld Court is a Centre for Sustainability run by a resident community with the help of short- and longer-term volunteers. Community members have full-time* jobs in the community in exchange for lodgings, food and a small stipend. Please see our website for details of the specific community member jobs which are currently vacant! As a registered educational charity, we offer education in sustainability through the learning, experience and practice of practical skills and community living.

We strive to maximise the productivity and the social benefits of our land and other resources, in a low-impact way. We generate income through a varied programme of educational courses, family activity holidays, venue hire and bed and breakfast/ hostel accommodation. The Court itself is a Victorian rectory (guest accommodation); community members live in a variety of dwellings including a strawbale cottage, yurts, a cladded caravan and the old stable block. Our grounds include an organically managed walled kitchen garden, fruit garden, small working farm, terraced lawns, woods, pasture and a stream. Volunteers work in our gardens, kitchen, grounds, house, woodshed, woodland and office in return for food, lodging (usually in single rooms) and a taste of communal living. The kitchen is vegetarian; we grow vegetables, fruit and our two-cow organic dairy produces milk, butter and cheese. Vegan and other diets are provided for. Most cooking and heating is wood-fuelled. Volunteers should be aware that some of the work is physically demanding. Facilities such as a well-stocked library, film projector and even a small "Pub" are available for evenings after work. Please visit our website for further information.

*The requirement of taking on a full-time role could possibly be more flexible in some cases, such as for families with young children. We welcome transparent discussion from the beginning with all of the community about how this could work for everyone whilst running a busy charity. However, it is important to point out that we don't have childcare facilities and do have to prioritise getting everything done.

World Wide Web *http://www.monktonwyldcourt.co.uk*

We are a diverse urban community and sometimes have spaces available for new members. We welcome people from all walks of life and would love to attract people with practical skills, as well as those with a head for figures.

The community was founded in 1981 to be a stable and secure home. It occupies two large semi-detached Victorian houses, with communal garden, in a quiet road in East London. Over thirty years later the community is still going strong. Our main commitments are to communal living and working by consensus. We are vegetarian and non-smoking at home, though some are non-veggie out of the home and smoke outside in the garden.

Our legal status is as a fully mutual housing co-op, and we make all decisions by consensus at monthly business meetings. Current members work and study full and part time, mainly in people-orientated positions within charities, mediation, healthcare, psychotherapy, eduacation, personal, professional and community development, and theatre. Some of us enjoy performing, theatre and cinema going, campaigning, keeping fit, lighting fires, travel, taking care of our beautiful home and garden.

We have no defined ideological focus but could loosely be described as greenish, leftish and feminist. The core values that are particularly important to us are: equality, integrity, respect, heart, fun, love, cooperation and consensus, supportive and caring, ethically engaged, honest communication, self-awareness, continuity, leftish, environmentally aware and sustainable, being the change, communal and sharing.

It takes time to join and settle in, and we aim to be fairly stable, so we ask all new members to stay for a minimum of two years. If we sound like the kind of community that you might like to join, do get in touch.

Mornington Grove Community

Postal Address
13 & 14 Mornington Grove
Bow, London E3 4NS

Telephone
020 8980 4534

Electronic Mail
morningtongrovecommunity
@yahoo.co.uk

Over 18s
11

Under 18s
0

Year started
1982

Situation
urban

Ideological focus
indefinable

Legal structure
company limited by shares

Open to new members?
yes

Charge visitors?
no

Work in lieu?
no

World Wide Web *http://www.morningtongrovecommunity.org.uk*

Newbold House

Postal Address
Newbold House
111 St Leonards Road
Forres IV36 2RE

Electronic Mail
office@newboldhouse.org

Over 18s
12

Under 18s
0

Year started
1979

Situation
rural/ edge of small town

Ideological focus
sustainable living, nature, wellbeing and open spirituality

Legal structure
co ltd by guarantee with charitable status

Open to new members?
yes

Charge visitors?
yes

Work in lieu?
yes

The Newbold Trust is a Wellbeing and Sustainable Living centre committed to 'Growing a Life Sustaining Society'. We are run by a residential community of around 10 permanent staff and up to 6 long and short term volunteers. We offer courses, retreats, a venue for local community groups and community living experiences, all with a focus on creating a positive and life sustaining society. The house is a beautiful late Victorian mansion with 7 acres of grounds, orchards, woodland and a large productive organic vegetable garden. We also have chickens and bees. We are on the outskirts of the pretty town of Forres, in close proximity to wonderful coastline, rivers and mountains. The Highland capital of Inverness is 26 miles away and easily accessible by public transport. We have close ties with the Findhorn Foundation ecovillage and community, which is just 5 miles away. We invite you to come and join us to experience what sustainable living means at Newbold. Whether for a few nights as a bed and breakfast guest, a longer stay on one of our programmes, as a community guest or a volunteer. If you are an educator or course leader with offerings which match our interests, we are always happy to discuss potential collaborations or venue hire with you. More details are available on our website or you can call or email us. Newbold House is a peaceful space to recharge your batteries, spend some time surrounded by nature, take part in a workshop or just live in community, exploring creative, sustainable ways of being and working together. We are open to long term volunteers year round and to short term volunteers between March and November. These opportunities book up quite far in advance. We often have more spaces on our Community Guest programme which allows you to work with us part time either mornings or afternoons 6 days per week in return for meals and a reduced rate on your accommodation. The Community Guest programme is perfect for those who want to experience community life while also having the freedom to explore the surrounding area and do their own thing. For more details check out our Community Guest page on our website. For details of our courses and workshops, please visit our website 'calendar of events'.

World Wide Web *http://www.newboldhouse.org*

Nutclough Housing Co-operative purchased the Nutclough Tavern (set in Hebden Bridge, in the beautiful Calder Valley, West Yorkshire) in December 2002. Current residents are seven adults, two children, one cat and thousands of bees (all called bee).

We live in a terrace row of four old cottages, with a long corridor knocked through upstairs. We each have a private bedroom. The rest of the building, which used to be a pub, is communal and we encourage neighbours, guests and the local community to enjoy the studio and large terraced hillside gardens.

Many of our members are performers, artists and activists so they are often away from home at weekends and over the summer. Our evening meals are vegetarian delights and we often have guests to eat and stay. We welcome visits from members of other co-ops. and love to share the beautiful woods on our doorstep.

We encourage prospective members to participate fully in the co-op. When a room becomes available all non-resident members are considered. We welcome contact from anyone wishing to know more. Nutclough Housing Co-operative is a member of Radical Routes, a network of co-operatives working for social change. Please contact us using email.

Nutclough Housing Co-op

Location
HX7 8HA

Electronic Mail
info@nutclough.org

Over 18s
7

Under 18s
2

Year started
2002

Situation
semi-rural

Ideological focus
ecological

Legal structure
industrial and provident society

Open to new members?
yes

Charge visitors?
yes

Work in lieu?
yes

World Wide Web *http://www.nutclough.org*

Oakfield Road Community

Postal Address
68a Oakfield Road
Stroud Green
London N4 4LB

Electronic Mail
oakfieldroad@
yahoogroups.co.uk

Over 18s
5

Under 18s
0

Year started
2000

Situation
urban

Ideological focus
practical, loosely liberal,
green with spiritual leanings

Legal structure
industrial and provident
society

Open to new members?
no

Charge visitors?
no

Work in lieu?
no

Oakfield Road Community is a small community established about 15 years ago and centred around sharing food (vegetarian) and tasks necessary for the upkeep of our house. We are situated in a quiet and leafy part of Stroud Green, North London about midway between Crouch End's more high end shopping and café culture and the more budget Harringay Green Lanes.

We rent direct from a private landlord, the ground floor and basement of a 4 storey Victorian terraced red brick house which includes a 125 square metre garden and patio overlooked by a balcony on the ground floor. At the time of writing the community consists of 1 woman and 4 men. Ages range from 25 to 52; occupations include: Buddhist plumber, children's entertainer, film industry software developer, jazz musician and psychologist working with wayward and autistic children. Members of our community are currently expected to cook about once a week. We do also meet about every 2 months with decisions in the interim being made via impromptu meetings and notices on our board. It is of course also important that members take some time to engage others socially, gaining in particular some awareness of the challenges and opportunities personally facing members, as well as those they deem more generally to be affecting the community.

To date our food arrangements have worked well. We have a shared bank account into which people are expected to make an agreed contribution for food and bills. We have also worked well socially. We could have better arrangements for the upkeep of the house and generally a greater investment in the developing, implementing and reviewing the community's procedures. In particular deciding on jobs to be done, sharing these out and then supporting each other to some sort of conclusion. Nevertheless we still have managed to get and retain people for on average about 2 to 3 years. Significantly longer, probably, than non-communally organised shared houses. Prospective members with previous experience would be particularly welcome.

We are a communal household of 8 people, and the house is so lovely that occupants tend to stay for 3-10 years before moving on. However sometimes we host volunteers or guests on short courses in Sheffield, and at other times the house is quieter when several people are away. This gives the house an ever changing rhythm between times when only a couple of people are around up to large communal meals when we have to extend the table.

Oakleigh

The mix of individuals brings a mix of personalities to the house, with interests ranging from music and green activism through to meditation, yoga and performance.

The house is privately owned, but everyone gets to have a say about changes. Housekeeping is managed in a flexible way, with a mix of communally purchased and private sharing of food, and a light-touch approach to recycling, cleaning and maintenance.

Location
S4 7AG

Telephone
0114 242 0344

Electronic Mail
*susannah.diamond
@gmail.com*

The house was bought in 2000 with support from the Ecology Building Society. It needed considerable work (plumbing, electrics, and a mixture of replacement double and secondary glazed windows etc.), but it is now a beautiful home. We made our restoration of the house as sympathetic and as low impact as possible, investing in eco-insulation, solar hot water, condensing boiler, efficient wood stove, low emission paints, and solar PV. More recent additions have included a pond (thank you, Julian!), raised beds for fruit and veg, and a temporary beehive.

Over 18s
8

Under 18s
0

Year started
2000

Situation
urban

We are located in Burngreave (a short distance from Sheffield town centre by bus, bike or on foot) and 5 minutes from shops and the Northern General Hospital. The house has a large garden with mature trees and birdsong and offers most amenities, including big screen film nights, but we don't have a television.

Ideological focus
none

Legal structure
unincorporated

Open to new members?
yes

Charge visitors?
no

Work in lieu?
no

Old Chapel Farm

Postal Address
Tylwych
Llanidloes SY18 6JR

Electronic Mail
franblockley
@yahoo.co.uk

Over 18s
8

Under 18s
0

Year started
2000

Situation
rural

Ideological focus
sustainability and more

Legal structure
*charity, co-operative,
company*

Open to new members?
yes

Charge visitors?
no

Work in lieu?
yes

We are a small land based community with many transient members from all walks of life who aspire to live simply in tune with land and seasons. Our 100 acres is an upland sheep farm which we manage more as a nature reserve.

Our focus is sustainability, biodiversity, creative lifestyle as well as connecting people to the land and we would like to find others who share some of our passions for the arts, agriculture, archaeology and the natural world to live here on a longer term basis.

We do some archaeology, produce most of our own vegetables, meat and milk, cheese and honey, wines, use alternative energy and have restored some beautiful old buildings. We manage our own woodlands for fuel and timber for our natural building projects. We run a programme of courses in prehistoric arts and traditional crafts and are reconstructing a working neolithic settlement.

We would like to create a welcoming and inspiring cultural/educational centre that will both provide a fulfilling way of life on the land and look for simple practical solutions to some of the challenges we face today in a rapidly changing world.

World Wide Web *http://oldchapelfarm.org*

We are a large community of people who share an old friary, and 70 acres of Suffolk farmland. We are nearly self sufficient in food and energy. Water is heated by a large wood fired biomass boiler we call the dragon and supplemented by a ground source heat pump (a gas fired boiler is used as a last resort). We have an array of 120 solar PV panels to provide our electricity and water comes from our own borehole with mains water back up. All the members have their own private rooms (family with 3 children likely to have 4 bedrooms plus living room; a single person may have 1 or 2 rooms depending on their invested capital). Most meals are eaten together in our big communal kitchen/dining room, using our own meat, vegetables, pulses and fruit. Meals are prepared under our rota job system by whoever signs up. If more vegetarians decide to cook then more meals will be vegetarian, if more meat eaters sign up then more meat will be consumed. The range of food is varied and excellent (special dietary needs catered for whenever possible). To make all this happen we each try to do around 15 hours community work a week. Jobs can be mundane or skilled – all are valuable! Community work includes milking, cheese making, construction projects, caring for the farm machinery and our animals, growing food, cooking, cleaning, sewing, maintaining the buildings, the orchards and the grounds and much more! Because of this communal commitment, members find that they need only work about three days a week outside the community to bring in enough money to pay bills. In summer months we enjoy help from WWOOFers from all over the world who stay for 2 weeks at a time (we can host up to 6 WWOOFers). They work alongside members who provide guidance on current outdoor tasks. Our own social events range from home cinema to play readings, panto to maypole dancing. To make our communal living work we have "Friday meetings" where we discuss ideas and make decisions by consensus. Sometimes, of course, we have conflict and disagreement – all part of the rich tapestry here!! The children and young people have a great life climbing trees, cycling, playing ball-games, baking bread, some like gardening! Budding musicians get together in the music room. Children in the main, walk or cycle to local schools.

Old Hall Community

Postal Address
Rectory Hill
East Bergholt
Colchester
CO7 6TG

Electronic Mail
secretary@oldhall.org.uk

Over 18s
45

Under 18s
9

Year started
1974

Situation
rural

Ideological focus
ecological

Legal structure
friendly society

Open to new members?
yes

Charge visitors?
yes

Work in lieu?
yes

World Wide Web *http://oldhall.org.uk*

Othona Essex

Here is a place where you can experience a different kind of holiday and go home with a fresh sense of well-being and community. It is inexpensive and our centre is in a beautiful and remote corner of Essex on the River Blackwater.

Nearby is the seventh-century Saxon chapel of St Peter-on-the-Wall which we use for twice daily informal worship. We run public events (weekends and weeks) on a variety of themes (e.g. art, music, drama, astronomy, spirituality) for all ages.

Our lifestyle is simple and non-dogmatic Christian. We welcome people of all faiths and of none. Our aim is that through open relationships and shared activities away from the pressures of modern life, we will reach a deeper understanding and acceptance of ourselves and others. We welcome individuals, families, school and church groups. To find out more, please get in touch.

Postal Address
East End Road
Bradwell-on-Sea
Southminster
CM0 7PN

Electronic Mail
bradwell@othona.org

Over 18s
5

Under 18s
0

Year started
1946

Situation
rural

Ideological focus
Christian; welcoming all faiths and none

Legal structure
registered charity

Open to new members?
yes

Charge visitors?
yes

Work in lieu?
yes

World Wide Web *http://www.othona-bradwell.org.uk*

Othona West Dorset is run by a small residential team who provide an experience of living in community for visitors staying in our 14-room community house, as they attend programmed events throughout the year. We see Othona as "A place to be real together".

While our roots are in the Christian heritage, we are open to all based on mutual respect and a sense of the everyday sacred. In approaching spirituality we are light-hearted, down to earth and unafraid to face change. Othona particularly suits people who are on a journey to discover their spiritual path or find a way to evolve within Christian faith. Some of us on team see ourselves as Christian and some do not, or acknowledge other faith traditions as a guiding presence. Within the team and visitors we affirm diversity among people in faith, spirituality, age, ability, race, background and sexual orientation.

For a new generation of retreat seekers we offer an informal community atmosphere, a simple lifestyle, and home cooking against a backdrop of great natural beauty. We schedule plenty of time for personal retreat in a community setting, often with creative arts. Othona is distinguished by the way visitors can join in a whole rhythm of life from gardening to leading chapel services. Singing, music, silence, candlelight and mindfulness are part of our life. Events during the school holidays are usually child friendly. Our stone house is set in 6 acres on the West Dorset coast and can accommodate 30 visitors. Located above the first natural World Heritage Site, Chesil Beach: walking, bird-watching and beachcombing are popular activities.

Othona West Dorset

Postal Address
Coast Road
Burton Bradstock
Bridport DT6 4RN

Telephone
01308 897130

Electronic Mail
recruitment
@othona-bb.org.uk

Over 18s
7

Under 18s
0

Year started
1965

Situation
rural and coastal

Ideological focus
Christian/spiritual

Legal structure
registered charity

Open to new members?
yes

Charge visitors?
yes

Work in lieu?
no

World Wide Web *http://www.othona-bb.org.uk*

Parsonage Farm

Parsonage Farm is a small community situated on the edge of the village of Burwell, twelve miles from Cambridge and five miles from Newmarket. Our community is much more about people, relationships and unity than it is about land, buildings and lifestyle.

Postal Address
Burwell
CB25

Electronic Mail
farm@parsonage1.plus.com

Over 18s
4

Under 18s
0

Year started
1971

Situation
rural

Ideological focus
none

Legal structure
-

Open to new members?
yes

Charge visitors?
no

Work in lieu?
no

Pendragon Community

Pendragon Community is a centre for low impact living and an experiment in living together happily. We aim for zero fossil fuel use. We are creative people who find community living enjoyable and care about sustainability. Long-term community members mainly have outside jobs, pay for their stay, and do not necessarily need to do anything at the community other than normal house cleaning and attending the weekly community meeting. However there is scope to keep animals and for community members to involve themselves in day to day running of the community and finding creative uses for our facilities including a large meeting room and outbuilding with potential for running day or residential workshops.

The organic garden and orchard is maintained by community volunteers and WWOOFers who can stay in a yurt or spare room. WWOOFers may also cook communal meals on certain days, do cleaning, house maintenance and building projects. We are omnivorous but there is a vegetarian fridge.

We are 5 minutes' walk from Glastonbury town centre, 10 minutes to the schools and 50 yards from a working organic dairy farm. Glastonbury is an eclectic town with a lively music scene, alternative culture and tourism.

The community was set up and is owned by me, Roger Dow (see his profile on the PendragonCommunity.com 'About Us' page). "I developed the house with the specific intention for it to be a sustainable community and I hope that it will become so well established that it will eventually outlive me. I believe that Climate Change is a serious problem that threatens quality of life for future generations. Community living is energy efficient and also brings people together so that they are less likely to be misled, providing a richer and more stable model for us to grow and find ourselves".

The house has 9 accommodations rooms, mostly en-suite, with wood burning stoves in every room, a biomass boiler for hot water, a woodburning Aga in the kitchen and a hybrid solar/wind system with charging for electric vehicles. In winter, managing wood for heating involves extra effort for those community members who are able to help. If we need to buy wood, community members share the cost, however free wood can sometimes be obtained.

Postal Address
*Pendragon House
Butleigh Road
Glastonbury BA6 8AQ*

Telephone
07810752835

Electronic Mail
*roger@
pendragoncommunity.com*

Over 18s
9

Under 18s
6

Year started
2013

Situation
urban

Ideological focus
sustainability

Legal structure
private ownership

Open to new members?
yes

Charge visitors?
no

Work in lieu?
no

World Wide Web *http://pendragoncommunity.com*

Pengraig Community

Postal Address
Pengraig Farm
Cwmpengraig, Drefach
Felindre
Llandysul
SA44 5HX

Electronic Mail
pengraig@gmail.com

Over 18s
10

Under 18s
0

Year started
2004

Situation
rural

Ideological focus
low impact, ecological, child friendly

Legal structure
unincorporated

Open to new members?
yes

Charge visitors?
yes

Work in lieu?
yes

We are an intentional community committed to living, working and having fun on an 80 acre organic farm in West Wales.

We have a forest garden with vegetable plots and bee hives. Over the years we have planted the field edges with native coppice, both adding to our wood supply and to the biodiversity of the land. We are also very proud of the disabled accessible woodland walk with its boardwalk, sensory garden, musical sculptures and bush craft centre.

We host camps and gatherings on the land which over the years have ranged from Womens' Camps, via Solstice Gatherings and the wonderful Wales Environmental Home Education Camp. We are consistently developing our facilities here. We've been working on the gathering field facilities and last year upgraded the compost toilets and added a new shower block. Finally the new wood fired central heating system is in (thank you NEST and the EST) and we are currently wrangling a low carbon grant for external wall insulation. Finally we are able to get on with decorating the house and updating the house kitchen. At the time of writing we are in a time of transition and therefore not accepting new members until we know what the new format will be.

We have no real shared ideology, though we hold vaguely similar attitudes in terms of environment, social justice, politics etcetera. The co-op was originally set up to accommodate people on low income in a traditionally wealthy area. Ploughshare Housing Co-op is based in a Victorian terraced house with small gardens to front and rear. It is in a quiet street in the heart of Bruntsfield, close to the Meadows and a short walk from the centre of Edinburgh.

Members of our Co-op, eight in total (at capacity, four men and four women, plus one cat) are both tenants and directors of the limited company that owns the building – we have no landlord. We also have no right to the proceeds if the co-op is wound-up. We have an organic box scheme, an ethical milkman and bulk-buy food for communal evening vegetarian meals from Green City.

Ploughshare Housing Co-op

Postal Address
16 Westhall Gardens
Bruntsfield
Edinburgh EH10 4JQ

Telephone
0131 229 1051

Electronic Mail
ploughsharehousingcoop
@gmail.com

Over 18s
8

Under 18s
0

Year started
1984

Situation
urban

Ideological focus
ecological

Legal structure
-

Open to new members?
yes

Charge visitors?
no

Work in lieu?
no

World Wide Web *http://ploughsharehousingco-opedinburgh.blogspot.com*

Postlip Community

Postal Address
Postlip Hall
Winchcombe
Cheltenham
GL54 5AQ

Electronic Mail
pha.cohousing@gmail.com

Over 18s
14

Under 18s
10

Year started
1970

Situation
rural

Ideological focus
none

Legal structure
industrial and provident society

Open to new members?
yes

Charge visitors?
no

Work in lieu?
yes

Postlip Hall is a beautiful, large, Grade 1 listed, Jacobean manor house with 15 acres of land, nestling in a quiet valley, surrounded by woods, just below the highest point in the Cotswolds. It's divided into eight family living units and members' ages range from 4 to 74. Most adults work outside Postlip and, although we all eat together fairly frequently, we live independent family lives. Postlip works as a Housing Association, meeting formally every month to discuss, plan, inform and make decisions.

Each family holds a long lease from the Association and can sell it back at an agreed valuation if they want to leave. The Association then recruits a new family to buy in by advertising.

Our legal structure means that you can only live here if you're a member and a leaseholder. We're sad that this stops us offering living space to other people, but we haven't been able to find a way around it. And we're also sad that our family-orientation means that it's hard to find room for long-term visitors or volunteers. We're set up to look after visitors on our monthly WWOOF weekends though, and very much enjoy having visitors then – we've been a WWOOF farm from the start.

We all pay a monthly ground rent, supplemented by income from the many events we organise, both in our magnificent 14th century tithe barn, from the annual Cotswold Beer Festival, to barn dances, folk music weekends and wedding celebrations to more intimate musical and dramatic performances in the main hall.

We work communally in our organic vegetable garden, look after our sheep, pigs and chickens and maintain and improve the woods, grounds and walls of the estate.

Children are an important part of being here and thrive in the space and the opportunities that life at Postlip offers them. We all try to live lightly on the earth and aim to leave Postlip a better place for those who follow. If you'd like to get to know Postlip better then the best way is to work alongside us on our monthly WWOOF weekends. Email us to find out more.

World Wide Web *http://www.postliphall.org.uk*

We are a community of 8 to 12 Quakers with a focus on leading a spirit-led life in an ecologically sustainable way. We run a range of led courses, events and retreats; these range from the reflective and spiritual to hands-on work in the 10 acres of reclaimed woodland, wetland, wild-flower meadow and organic fruit and vegetable gardens which we have managed since the Community was started in 1988.

We also welcome individuals on self-catering retreats, and self-catering or catered groups of up to 16 (if sharing – more if also camping). We are in beautiful semi-rural surroundings in the Peak District, with a wide range of hill and riverside walks from the doorstep and bus and train links to Sheffield and Manchester.

We review our on-going membership on a three-yearly basis and are open to membership enquiries from Quakers and attenders.

Quaker Community

Postal Address
Water Lane
Bamford
Hope Valley S33 0DA

Telephone
01433 650085

Electronic Mail
mail@
quakercommunity.org.uk

Over 18s
9

Under 18s
0

Year started
1988

Situation
semi-rural

Ideological focus
Quaker

Legal structure
i&ps

Open to new members?
yes

Charge visitors?
yes

Work in lieu?
no

World Wide Web *http://www.quakercommunity.org.uk*

Random Camel Housing Co-op

Postal Address
27 Foundation Street
Ipswich IP4 1BQ

Electronic Mail
randomcamel
@phonecoop.coop

Over 18s
8

Under 18s
2

Year started
2012

Situation
urban

Ideological focus
progressive social
change, ecological, diy

Legal structure
industrial and provident
society

Open to new members?
yes

Charge visitors?
no

Work in lieu?
no

Random Camel Housing Co-op of Ipswich, Suffolk, purchased 23-27 Foundation Street, Ipswich in 2012. It's a terrace of three 2-up 2-down properties, two of which have been knocked through, one remaining as a self-contained entity. In all, it can house up to 9 tenants. The house is versatile, spacious – big rooms and lots of storage spaces – rather worn in terms of decoration, or in the midst of eco-refurb.

Our co-op is a great opportunity for a group of people to create a base of community action and live as an intentional community. The houses have calm and quiet days, bustling renovation days, crazy parties and regular guests, visitors and events. It's in the middle of town but standing in the rose and honeysuckle back gardens it feels like a secluded oasis. The rooms are different sizes and types and most need some level of work. We try to live sustainably, in as low impact fashion as possible in an urban environment.

We are veggies and vegans. We recycle a lot, compost, re-use, help run a food co-operative we founded in 2007 where we get our wholefoods, help out at a Community Supported Agriculture Scheme we helped start a few years ago, run work days to do work on the houses, and work with a few different local environmental and other groups. We have had events at the houses including film screenings, prisoner letter writing groups, hosted bazaars, music gigs, women's groups, neighbourhood tea parties, massage sessions and more.

Future plans include linking up with the Energy Co-op that the Transition Town group is starting, we'd like to build a compost loo and run training courses on the eco-renovations that we've learnt, an info centre and zine library, band practice space, passive solar extension and lots more events. We like to meet like-minded people and like nothing better than when our house is buzzing with people, being inspired and informed.

World Wide Web *http://randomcamelcoop.blogspot.com*

Redfield is an intentional community situated in North Buckinghamshire. We live as a single household in a large old mansion, set in 17 acres of gardens, woodland and pasture, surrounded by farmland. We have sheep, pigs, chickens and bees.

Redfield

Life here involves a lot of sharing, commitment, responsibility, building maintenance, gardening, animal management, logging and having fun. The ground floor of the house and the grounds are communal, with private rooms and units on the first and second floors.

The Redfield Centre is a separate self contained venue with accommodation spaces and a classroom space with a workshop attached which could be hired for similar minded groups/ individuals (please visit the Redfield Centre website for more info www.redfieldcentre.wordpress.com).

We all have part-time jobs and pay a monthly rent to the co-op; we commit a minimum of 16 hours per week to the community. In recent years, members' outside jobs have included accountancy, forestry, lecturing, planning, nursing, teaching, lorry driving, and care work. Members also run their own businesses from the Community, these currently include making and selling canvas tents via World Tents, teaching music, wood milling, photography, yoga classes and massage therapy.

Redfield is a registered Housing Co-operative and we make all our decisions by consensus at our fortnightly meeting. We welcome visitors on our quarterly visitor days, as WWOOFers or as volunteers during our two maintenance weeks of the year. We also run "Living in Community" weekends for an inside view of community living.

Postal Address
Buckingham Rd, Winslow Buckingham MK18 3LZ

Telephone
01296 713661

Electronic Mail
info@ redfieldcommunity.org.uk

Over 18s
15

Under 18s
8

Year started
1978

Situation
rural

Ideological focus
community life and sustainability

Legal structure
i&ps

Open to new members?
yes

Charge visitors?
yes

Work in lieu?
yes

World Wide Web *http://www.redfieldcommunity.org.uk*

Sanford Housing Co-op

Postal Address
11 Sanford Walk
London
SE14 6NB

Electronic Mail
mark.langford@cds.coop

W e have beautiful ponds, gardens and a friendly atmosphere, a tropical communal oasis in London with a famous colourful peace movement mural. Many performers and artists live here and we have tried to artistically redesign our living space.

Founded in 1973 it was built using private finance supplied by the Housing Corporation and Commercial Union. Sanford Housing Co-op consists of 122 units of shared accommodation in 14 purpose-built houses. Its rents are not set by any outside body but are designed to cover actual costs. All the tenants as members of the Co-operative are collectively landlords and responsible for helping the Co-op to protect their interests and to save the Co-op money by their voluntary work.

Sanford actively seeks applicants from all sections of the community, over the age of 18, who wish to live in a Co-operative, regardless of gender, ethnic origin, disability, sexual orientation or health status. Sanford is a single person co-operative and is not suitable for applicants who have dependent children or who wish to live as a couple.

Over 18s
122

Under 18s
0

Year started
1973

Situation
urban

Ideological focus
none

Legal structure
industrial and provident society

Open to new members?
yes

Charge visitors?
no

Work in lieu?
no

We are the newest housing co-op in Sheffield. In our house costs and responsibilities are shared. It is run on co-operative principles. We are a vegetarian household and share cooking and costs of food. We are striving to live sustainably and are working for peace and social change. We're part of the Radical Routes network. If you are interested in knowing more about us get in touch

Share Instead

Postal Address
49 Steade Road
Sheffield S7 1DS

Telephone
0114 2587073

Electronic Mail
shareinstead@gmail.com

Over 18s
5

Under 18s
0

Year started
2012

Situation
urban

Ideological focus
working for peace and social change

Legal structure
a registered society (previously I&PS)

Open to new members?
yes

Charge visitors?
yes

Work in lieu?
no

Springhill Cohousing Community

Postal Address
Springfield Road
Stroud
GL5 1TN

Electronic Mail
info@
springhillcohousing.com

Over 18s
50

Under 18s
32

Year started
2000

Situation
urban

Ideological focus
cohousing/consensus

Legal structure
company limited by shares

Open to new members?
yes

Charge visitors?
yes

Work in lieu?
no

Springhill Cohousing is the first new build Cohousing Community in the UK and the first project of the Cohousing Company. The search for land started in 1999 and the site in Stroud was acquired in 2000. Very soon after, all the plots were pre-sold to members who designed the community and layout of their own houses/flats.

The principles of Cohousing are consensus decision making, pedestrianised estate, large common house for shared evening meals, private self-contained units. The 35 houses, flats and studios are super-insulated, 20 houses have 49 kWp of PV solar panels. There is a car share scheme and the site is in the town centre.

There are a number of committees eg. Kitchen, Garden, Parking, Disputes etc. which are mandated to make decisions. The idea is to reduce the number of large meetings and trust small groups to make decisions. Joining is by self selection. The only criteria are that the new members agree with the principles of Cohousing and can afford to buy in. There are often rooms available for lodgers and houses and flats become available to rent or buy from time to time. Please register interest via the web site.

World Wide Web *http://www.springhillcohousing.com*

Talamh is Gaelic for Earth, and its 50 acres form a green haven just north of the Southern Uplands. The thousands of young trees planted over the past two decades are growing into woodland and the pond we created teems with life – the land here provides a mixed habitat for wildlife. Talamh is currently home to 6 adults who live in the 17th century listed farmhouse, caravans and living vehicles around the paddock. We share food and cooking, eating together in the evenings and some lunchtimes. We make cakes and jams, partly to use up the masses of homegrown fruit. We make bread sometimes and grow vegetables, keep hens for eggs and burn lots of wood in wintertime to try and keep us and the buildings warm. Important decisions are made by consensus at meetings, but a lot of informal discussion takes place at mealtimes or around the fire. There is always plenty to do here, but the most crucial project at the moment is an extensive program of renovation. Talamh functions in an informal, unstructured way, and plenty of self-motivation is required, combined with a communicative, co-operative approach.

We are into: working towards sustainability and low-impact living, looking after our land and encouraging wildlife and biodiversity, growing our own veg and fruit, repairing our buildings, opposing Trident, playing music, eating good food, looking out for each other, working to resolve conflict, laughing about stuff round the fire and eating chips.

Outdoor events are hosted several times a year – discussion groups, skillshare events, gatherings. There is lots of space for camping and a visitor caravan that sleeps 8. Volunteers are welcome to visit by arrangement, to help out with the work here and experience community life: contact talamhvolunteering@gmail.com for more information.

Talamh

Postal Address
Birkhill House
Coalburn
ML11 0NJ

Electronic Mail
talamh@lineone.net

Over 18s
6

Under 18s
0

Year started
1993

Situation
rural

Ideological focus
diy/environmental

Legal structure
industrial and provident society

Open to new members?
yes

Charge visitors?
no

Work in lieu?
yes

World Wide Web *http://www.talamh.org.uk*

Taraloka Buddhist Retreat Centre for Women

Postal Address
Taraloka Retreat Centre
Bettisfield
Whitchurch
SY13 2LD

Electronic Mail
admin@taraloka.org.uk

Over 18s
12

Under 18s
0

Year started
1985

Situation
rural

Ideological focus
Buddhist

Legal structure
registered charity

Open to new members?
no

Charge visitors?
yes

Work in lieu?
no

Taraloka is both a community and a Buddhist retreat centre for women, to which women come from all over the world to practise meditation and go deeper into the teachings of the Buddha. The centre has been running since 1985 and offers a beautiful environment in which to practise stillness and simplicity.

All of us living here are committed to Buddhist ideals and to creating the best possible facilities for women to come on retreat. For the purposes of our work, people have individual responsibilities for different work areas, for example cooking, maintenance or leading retreats. We all actively pursue the Buddhist way of life, following a daily programme of meditation, work and communal meals. We live simply and communally with a strong emphasis on ethical practice, aiming for more kindness, generosity, contentment, truthful speech and clarity of mind. Apart from our respective team meetings, we hold weekly community meetings and business meetings. We aim to be friendly and co-operative and decisions are arrived at through consensus.

Taraloka is registered as a charity and all members receive the same basic support. We are all part of the Buddhist Movement the Triratna Buddhist Community and we don't have a system for accommodating volunteers from outside of the movement to work here.

We have a range of retreats, some for those who are completely new to meditation and Buddhism, and some for those who currently practice within our tradition. We also have an Open Day every two years. For further information about our retreats please contact the office or see our website.

World Wide Web *http://www.taraloka.org.uk*

Tariki is a community of people who believe that Buddhism is something which we live, not simply a practice to be done in limited time slots during a busy day. Buddhism is the spirit which flows in our bones and the beautiful vibrancy of the world we encounter. It is the possibility for awakening to the wonder of the ordinary and to cease searching the ends of the earth for jewels which are already in our possession.

The Tariki Community centres around a large house in Narborough near Leicester. Although we no longer have as large a long term community as we used to have, we now see our role as being to offer a range of activities to the locality and to professional groups and to offer a place for people to come for short term residential stays for retreat, writing intensives, transitional times and interim life phases. We are also the hub for like-minded people, offering events, gatherings and space for a network of people with common interests.

Tariki Trust runs a Buddhist psychotherapy training programme out of the house on which house residents teach. It also runs a therapy service. Residents are also involved with various social and environmental projects in Leicester and provide chaplaincy to hospitals and colleges.

We share practical tasks looking after visitors and maintaining house and garden. We aim to create a community of people who are interested in learning, ideas, creativity and social responsibility and welcome the involvement of others in this project.

Tariki Trust

Postal Address
The Buddhist House
12 Coventry Road,
Narborough
Leicester LE19 2GR

Telephone
0116 286 7476

Electronic Mail
courses@tarikitrust.org

Over 18s
4

Under 18s
0

Year started
2012

Situation
semi-rural

Ideological focus
Buddhist

Legal structure
registered charity

Open to new members?
yes

Charge visitors?
yes

Work in lieu?
no

World Wide Web *http://www.tarikitrust.org*

Temple Druid Community

Postal Address
Llandilo
Clunderwen
SA66 7XS

Electronic Mail
info@templedruid.org

Over 18s
6

Under 18s
3

Year started
2014

Situation
rural

Ideological focus
Eclectic

Legal structure
ltd company, not for profit

Open to new members?
yes

Charge visitors?
yes

Work in lieu?
yes

Temple Druid community formed in the spring of 2014 when we heard that Temple Druid House and land was going to be sold. We formed a company with the express intention of purchasing Temple Druid and of developing a year round source of high quality organic food and a therapeutic holistic retreat centre for disadvantaged children/families and vulnerable adults.

Our long term goals include having several new members joining us over the next 5-10 years, developing sustainable ecological housing through restoration of barns, out-houses and self builds – eventually becoming an eco-village community under the Welsh "One Planet" Policy.

At the time of writing we are interested in people with some capital to invest in order to pay off existing loans. After this we may be in a position to offer membership to those without capital investment. Whilst it is not necessary to have experience in a particular area of community living and renovations, the current community would greatly benefit from people with those skills.

For further information see our website, and "events" page for New Member days.

World Wide Web *http://www.templedruid.org*

Established in 1982, 301 Housing Cooperative consists of seven flats based in two large Victorian houses in the Chapeltown area of Leeds. 301 is run collectively by its members with monthly general meetings, subgroup meetings and with individual roles as required.

301's aim is to provide supportive comfortable and affordable housing to people in housing need. Due to our low turnover we do not operate a waiting list, but advertise widely locally and on the Leeds Housing Co-ops blog: http://leedshousingcoops.blogspot.co.uk when vacancies do arise.

301 Housing Co-op

Postal Address
301-303 Chapeltown Rd
Leeds
LS7 3JT

Electronic Mail
claireharbottle
@googlemail.com

Over 18s
7

Under 18s
0

Year started
1982

Situation
rural

Ideological focus
ecological

Legal structure
company limited by guarantee

Open to new members?
no

Charge visitors?
no

Work in lieu?
no

Threshold Centre

T he Threshold Centre at Cole Street Farm is a unique, pioneering cohousing community and sustainable education centre. We aim to 'walk our talk' with a lifestyle that is more green, more affordable, and more neighbourly.

The Threshold Centre consists of fourteen dwellings, seven of which are affordable rent and shared ownership with a local housing association – a first in the short history of cohousing in this country.

There is also a common house with shared facilities and guest rooms, green energy systems and a community market garden.

We run regular weekend workshops to provide a co-housing experience alongside gardening, permaculture, meditation, mindfulness practice and fun!

Please see our website or email us for more details of courses or vacancies.

Postal Address
Cole Street Farm
Cole Street Lane
Gillingham
SP8 5JQ

Electronic Mail
info@
thresholdcentre.org.uk

Over 18s
19

Under 18s
1

Year started
2004

Situation
rural

Legal structure
company limited by shares

Open to new members?
yes

Charge visitors?
no

Work in lieu?
no

World Wide Web *http://www.thresholdcentre.org.uk*

Tinkers Bubble is a small woodland community which uses environmentally sound methods of working the land without fossil fuels. We have planning permission for self-built houses on the condition that we make a living from the land. We make our monetary incomes mainly through forestry, apple work and gardening. As a result we're money poor but otherwise rich! We manage about 28 acres of douglas fir, larch, and mixed broadleaf woodland using horses, two person saws, and a wood-fired steam-powered sawmill. Our pastures, orchards, and gardens are organically certified, and no-dig methods are commonly used. We press apple juice for sale, grow most of our own vegetables, keep chickens and bees, and sell our produce at farmers markets. We make loads of jam, cheese, butter, preserves, cider and wine. We have solar powered 12V electricity, spring water on tap, and use compost toilets. We burn wood for cooking, heating, and for hot water in the bathhouse. We eat some meat (mostly game), and try to cater for all diets. Though some of us would consider ourselves to be spiritual, we have no shared spirituality. Most people wash their clothes by hand. Life is lived mostly outdoors, so it's cold in the winter, but we live on the top of a steep hill, so there's plenty of chances to get warm! There's loads of wildlife on site, particularly badgers, deer and ticks!

We're currently a group of 10 adults, spanning a wide age range, and 2 young children. We are open to new live-in members who are interested in making a living from the land. Please get in touch by email or post if you would like to volunteer with us, including why you're interested in visiting, and any relevant experience you've got. We don't expect you to be a professional peasant; It just helps to get an idea of what you're about. Please check your spam folder for our response – we answer all emails, usually within a week or so, but some email providers (particularly hotmail) seem to put all emails from riseup.net in the spam folder! We have a guest house with a wood burner, but long-johns are still a must in winter. Bring a torch, warm clothes, practical footwear, and any fresh looking roadkill you find en-route. Follow the Tinkers bubble blog.

Tinker's Bubble

Postal Address
Norton Covert
Little Norton
Norton sub Hamdon
Stoke-sub-Hamdon
TA14 6TE

Electronic Mail
tinkersbubble@riseup.net

Over 18s
10

Under 18s
2

Year started
1994

Situation
rural

Ideological focus
Environmental

Legal structure
-

Open to new members?
yes

Charge visitors?
yes

Work in lieu?
yes

World Wide Web *http://*tinkersbubble.wordpress.com

Tipi Valley

Postal Address
Cwmdu
Talley
Llandeilo
SA19 7EE

Electronic Mail
revrmayes@hotmail.co.uk

Over 18s
50

Under 18s
30

Year started
1974

Situation
rural

Ideological focus
ecological

Legal structure
unincorporated

Open to new members?
yes

Charge visitors?
no

Work in lieu?
no

To be honest, we're a bunch of about 70 hippies, some of us 'originals'. Tipi Valley is high in the Welsh hills, on 200 acres that we have bought bit by bit together over 40 years. Our oldest land has already reverted to temperate rainforest. The idea is that we are part of nature, living within nature. Thus all our homes are low-impact dwellings such as tipis, yurts, domes and thatched or turf-roofed round houses. We are a village, not a commune, and everyone is responsible for their own economy. We do not have regular business meetings, only necessary ones, and we never vote. It works by consensus and personal relationships. Dogs are not welcome. And cats have a very negative impact on the environment. Village spirituality is natural, the simple paganism of celebrating our total dependence on Mother Earth, mostly expressed in chanting and drumming at the sweatlodge and at Big Lodge social get-togethers, and Saturday night music jams. Over 120 home births. Education at local Welsh-speaking schools, and home education. It's a survival lifestyle, 100% nature.

We have a large communal tipi called the 'Big Lodge' where we gather and where guests may usually stay to experience the lifestyle first-hand. Bring sufficient warm bedding, a roll-mat to sleep on (we use sheepskins) and food; also a good torch and candles. You look after yourself, cooking over the open fire on the stone hearth in the middle of the Big Lodge, fetching water from the well, gathering firewood, and cutting fresh rushes for the floor. It's an amazing primitive experience, living around the hearth in a round dwelling, but if you don't think you can cope with it, maybe you should bring a tent and pitch it close by the Big Lodge instead. We don't want any payment and we don't run a WWOOFing scheme of work in exchange for food etc. You must provide your own food. We do not expect you to work for us other than helping to keep the Big Lodge a tidy and welcoming place. Parking is very limited. If you bring your vehicle then e-mail first and we'll send you a map showing where you can park. Take a look at the Tipi Valley page on the D&D website where there's usually a lot more information about visiting.

World Wide Web *http://www.tipivalley.co.uk*

Trelay is a small cohousing community in North Cornwall. It is a wonderful place to live! We currently have 20 adults and 8 children. We each have our own private living space and there are several community buildings and 30 acres of land. We aim towards environmental, social and financial sustainability.

Trelay

Trelay is set in a beautiful location with sea views. There are wild flowers and butterflies in profusion. The peace and quiet, the ravens and buzzards, starry skies and occasional gales calm or stir the spirit.

Trelay members hold equity in their living space, and share the land and a number of communal buildings. The ground floor of the farmhouse, where we often meet for communal meals, has a large kitchen and dining room. The Games Room has table tennis and pool tables, and can be cleared for music and dancing. The Green Barn has a range of communal workshop and storage facilities. There is a large polytunnel with a second one planned, garden sheds and a laundry with shared washing machines and dryers.

Postal Address
Trelay Farm
St Gennys
Bude EX23 0NJ

Telephone
01840 230482

Electronic Mail
jackie@trelay.org

We have several dozen fruit trees, an extensive soft fruit area, a large communal vegetable patch. Small groups take responsibility for animals. We have 3 ponies, 2 Dexter cows with 2 calves, 6 Zwartbles sheep with 6 Lambs, 2 pigs with 16 piglets and chickens.

Over 18s
20

Under 18s
8

We have two acres of woodland and a shared log store. Trelay has a private sewage system which is being developed into a series of reedbeds. There is a PV roof and more renewable energy projects are under discussion.

Year started
2007

Situation
coastal / rural

Ideological focus
sustainability

We're a happy little community with lots of big ideas for new projects, If you'd like to know more there are several ways of getting involved:
- Interest weekends
- Courses
- Festivals
- Working Volunteer weeks
See our website for more details.

Legal structure
company limited by guarantee

Open to new members?
yes

Charge visitors?
yes

Work in lieu?
yes

World Wide Web *http://www.trelay.org*

Woodhead Community

Postal Address
Kinloss
Forres
IV36 2UE

Electronic Mail
info@woodheadcom.org

Over 18s
6

Under 18s
0

Year started
1994

Situation
rural

Ideological focus
*collectively living
with spirit*

Legal structure
unincorporated

Open to new members?
yes

Charge visitors?
yes

Work in lieu?
yes

After over 20 successful years as a small family and land-based community near the Findhorn Foundation, change is at hand in the Woodhead Community. Our children have grown up and moved on, and we are looking to welcome new people into our group.

Our buildings offer living space for up to 12 people, and the group is a mix of currently six long-term adults and others who might stay for any time between a few weeks and a few years.

Our communal facilities include a shower room and a big kitchen/dining room used for our shared meals, as well as a big vegetable garden and food storage space. As part of managing the garden we offer wwoofing work exchange during the gardening season.

We endeavour to balance the needs of individually earning a living with the joys and challenges of being in close relationship, sharing resources and growing our own food. Besides the sharing of community responsibilities, we also engage in artistic, political and ecological debate and action. We encourage clear and honest interaction, and a growing personal awareness of what moves us spiritually.

We want to continue our shared life with a broad cultural and age range of people. Currently our communal rhythms include shared cooking for evening meals, food-buying, car-pool and working together once a week. We also welcome new inspiration and input.

OTHER EXISTING COMMUNITIES

Communards are busy people and filling out questionnaires isn't always a priority for them. We asked places to opt in to our printed directory but didn't hear from quite a lot of communities that – at the time of writing – still had a listing on our website.
We're aware that, over time, our printed publications become quite a valuable historical resource so in the interests of completeness we're also including here minimalist listings for those other communities (with website addresses if we have them).

The Abbey
OX14 4AF
www.theabbey.uk.com

Balnakeil Craft Village
IV27 4PT

Banna Lesbian Housing Co-operative
NG1 9GR
bannahousingcoop.wordpress.com

Beech Grove Community
CT15 4HH
www.bruderhof.com

Bhaktivedanta Manor
WD25 8EZ
www.krishnatemple.com

Blackcurrent
NN1 4JQ
www.blackcurrentcentre.org.uk

Botton Village
YO21 2NJ
www.cvt.org.uk/botton-village

Brambles Housing Co-op
S3 9EH

Branches Housing Co-operative
BD7 1JP

Brotherhood Church
WF8 3DF
www.thebrotherhoodchurch.org

Camphill Rudolf Steiner Schools
AB15 9EP
www.camphillschools.org.uk

Catholic Worker Farm
WD3 9J
www.thecatholicworkerfarm.org

Chickenshack Housing Co-op
LL36 9NH

Coed Hills Rural Artspace
CF71 7DP
www.coedhills.co.uk/

Cymuned Y Chwarel
SY20 9AZ
www.cat.org.uk

The Drive Housing Co-op
E17 3BW
www.thedrive.coop

Equino Housing Co-op
M13 0PQ
www.eqn.co.uk

Faslane Peace Camp
G84 8NT
faslanepeacecamp.wordpress.com

Findhorn Foundation
IV36 3TZ
www.findhorn.org

Frankleigh House
BA15 2PB

Fruit Corner
BS6 6BU

Gaunts House Community
BH21 4JQ
www.gauntshouse.com

Giroscope
HU3 6BH
www.giroscope.co.uk

Glyn Abbey
SA15 5TL

Golem Housing Co-operative
SA1 6AB
golemcoop.blogspot.co.uk

Grow Heathrow
UB7 0JH
www.transitionheathrow.com

The Hive Housing Co-op
BD1 3EJ

Inverness L'Arche Community
IV2 4QR
larcheinvernessnews.blogspot.com

Iona Community
PA76 6SN
www.iona.org.uk

Ipswich L'Arche Community
IP1 3QU
larcheipswich.co.uk

Lambeth L'Arche Community
SE27 9JU
www.larchelondon.org.uk

Lammas
SA34 0YD
www.lammas.org.uk

The Land of Roots
DH7 8EN

Laughton Lodge
BN8 6BY
www.laughtonlodge.org

Lothlorien Community
DG7 3DR
www.lothlorien.tc

Newton Dee Camphill Village
AB15 9D
www.newtondee.org.uk

Pennine Camphill Community
WF4 3JL
www.pennine.ac.uk

Plants For A Future
PL22 0QJ
www.pfaf.org

Rainbow Housing Co-op
MK13 0DW

Rose Howey Housing
Co-operative
L8
rosehowey.org.uk

Rubha Phoil Forest Garden
IV45 8RS
www.skye-permaculture.org.uk

Sahaja
SP3 5DJ

Shekinashram
BA6 8BZ
www.shekinashram.org

Shrub Family
NR16 2QT

Skylark Housing Co-op
BN2
www.skylarkhousingcoop.org.uk

Stepping Stones Housing
Co-operative
NP25 4L
www.highburyfarm.freeserve.co.uk

Steward Community Woodland
TQ13 8SD
www.stewardwood.org

Stourbridge Camphill Houses
DY8 3YA
www.cvt.org.uk/stourbridge

Summerhill Housing
Co-operative
NE4 6EB

Taliesin Housing
Co-operative
SY20 8JH

Tan-y-Fron Housing
Co-operative
SY22 6BP
tanyfronhousingcoop.wordpress.com

Tangram Housing Co-op
LS8 5AD
www.tangramhousing.co.uk/

Torch Housing Co-op
B18 5NH

Ty'r Eithin
SA15 5BR

The Well at Willen
MK15 9AA
www.thewellatwillen.org.uk

West End Housing
Co-operative
NE4 5NL
www.westendhousingco-op.co.uk

Whiteway Colony
GL6 7EP

Wild Futures Monkey
Sanctuary
PL13 1NZ
www.wildfutures.org

Windsor Hill Wood
BA4 4JE
www.windsorhillwood.co.uk

Youkoso
N16 6HT

FORMING COMMUNITIES

*These are all groups that have been going for a period of time...
but haven't quite moved in yet!*

We have detailed planning permission to convert Cannock Mill near Colchester to our common house and build 23 Passivhaus homes. We aim to develop a mutually supportive community, living in our own low energy homes, with some shared facilities. We want to encourage social contact and individual space, in a community managed by ourselves. Membership is open to all ages and backgrounds. So far we're mainly professional people (55+) with a wide range of jobs and diverse individual pursuits. We have a mutual 'getting to know you' process in place. We move forward to a building phase: new homes, new members and a new commitment to developing the best possible way of co-operating and contributing to the community. Our website gives further information about us and about cohousing generally. We were formally known as London Countryside Cohousing Group but in August 2015 we changed our name to Cannock Mill Cohousing Colchester Ltd.

Cannock Mill Cohousing

Location
East Anglia
Electronic Mail
*enquiries@
cannockmillcohousingcolchester.
co.uk*

World Wide Web *http://cannockmillcohousingcolchester.co.uk*

Norwich Cohousing

Location
East Anglia
Electronic Mail
*info@
norwichcohousing.org.uk*

We've purchased a plot of land at Sussex Street just north of the city centre, and formed a Community Interest Company to take the project forward. The site already has planning permission for 17 two and three-bedroom units, plus 2,500 square feet of communal space. The units are likely to be all open market or privately rented unless we can engage with a housing association. The site is urban, so outside space is limited, but it's in a lovely street with the river nearby and opportunities for getting involved in local allotments or forming a community garden. The city centre is in walking distance, and Norwich is a great city to live in – not too big and not too small! There are schools nearby and the University is in cycling distance. The approved plans are for high quality housing, south facing, and will be at or close to passivhaus standard. Best of all, the local community organisation were very involved in the design, and so are interested and positive about the development. For more info, plans and (eventually) prices, see our website.

World Wide Web *http://www.norwichcohousing.org.uk*

Red Pig Farm

Location
Wales
Electronic Mail
redpig@agroecology.co.uk

We are currently looking for additional members and further investment for the first Agroecology Land Initiative project at Red Pig Farm, Llandeilo, Wales. The Agroecology Land Initiative is an organisation created to advocate and implement agroecological methods in the UK to help secure food sovereignty, energy independence, and environmental regeneration in a way that is financially viable and socially just. We aim to create a model of co-sufficient community farming and forestry to demonstrate the benefits of communal low-impact living for the creation of rural enterprise. To achieve this we have developed an innovative membership based equity investment scheme for co-housing co-operative that will allow for different levels of investment while retaining a principle of common ownership. If this is something that interests you then please feel free to attend our OPEN DAY 20TH JUNE 2015. For more information about the open day and to download our brochure and business plan visit our website or e-mail us.

World Wide Web *http://agroecology.co.uk*

We own 22 acres of woodland and pasture in Herefordshire and are creating an ecological and personal growth commune. We will be off-grid and will manage the woodland and use timber from it to build a community house big enough for 10 adults plus children. We have an architect working with us and will be putting in for planning permission (we already have permission for a round-wood timber framed barn). We have a Woodland Management Plan ready to be authorised by the Forestry Commission and are working with Herefordshire Wildlife Trust to create a plan for protecting and enhancing the wildlife. We aim to be self-sufficient in food and are working with permaculturists to achieve this. We are vegan and tolerant of vegetarians. We are forming the Living Land Trust, which will own the land and the buildings and intend that the majority of participants will live and work here. We are open to new participants who want to live and work on the land, and who are committed to their personal growth and to that of those they will be living with.

Elysian Fields

Location
The Midlands
Electronic Mail
amila@houseoflove.org.uk

Seeking Intentional Community Pioneers: We are developing an intentional community initially based near Cambridge and looking for an inspiring pioneering team. It will be a humble and hardworking residential community, which includes accommodation in two shepherd's huts, two rooms in a converted stable and a caravan. The community will be sustained through commercial endeavour (see www.themissingsock.co.uk and www.kindahappy.org). The aim is to have an intentional community supportive of the charity The Missing Kind (www.missingkind.org). We are looking for interactive fun-loving people with a passion for wellbeing, catering, entertainment, housekeeping, administration, maintenance, gardening and animal care. All food, accommodation and a monthly allowance will be provided for a fair exchange. There is no attachment to any specific sectors or faiths, but a focus is on wellbeing for self and others is important. If you are interested, check out the links above, as it is essential those applying breathe our ethos.

The Missing Kind

Location
East Anglia
Electronic Mail
h@themissingsock.co.uk

World Wide Web *http://missingkind.org*

OTHER FORMING COMMUNITIES

It can take years to set up a new intentional community and forming groups can have periods of both intense and very little activity. Others groups are set up on a whim and have relatively short lives. In the interests of historical completeness we're also including here minimalist listings for groups that haven't responded to our recent enquiries but – at the time of writing – still have a listing on our website.

Abundant Earth Community
The Midlands
abundantearthcommunity.blogspot.
co.uk

Alive Fifty Plus
North of England

Black Combe Housing Co-op
North of England

Black Dragon Co-op
Wales

Brighton Cohousing
South East England
www.brightoncohousing.org.uk

Cambridge K1 Cohousing
East Anglia
www.cambridge-k1.co.uk

ClanAlba Housing Co-op
Scotland

Coastal Community
South West England
www.coastalcommunity.org.uk

Cobweb Housing Co-op
The Midlands
cobwebhousing.wordpress.com

Cohousing Cardiff
Wales
cohousingcardiff.co.uk

Cohousing Northern Ireland
Northern Ireland

Cohousing Woodside
South East England
cohousingwoodside.co.uk

Culdees
Scotland
www.culdees-ecovillage.co.uk

Curney Bank Commonwealth
The Midlands

Earthlight Community
Wales

Eco Village Cymru
Wales
ecovillagecymru.wordpress.com

Eco-Hamlet
Wales
www.eco-hamlets.org.uk

Enlinca
East Anglia
www.enlinca.org.uk

Five Rivers Cohousing
North of England

Freeriver
South West England
www.freerivercommunity.com

Mandorla Cohousing
The Midlands
www.mandorlacoho.wordpress.com

Older Women's Cohousing London
South East England
www.owch.org.uk

Plotgate Venture
South West England
www.plotgate.org.uk

Prospect Permaculture Community
South West England
www.prospectcommunity.org.uk

Red Macgregor Housing Co-operative
Scotland

Scargill House
North of England
www.scargillmovement.org

Shangrileeds
North of England
www.shangrileeds.wordpress.com

Still Green
South East England
stillgreenweb.org

Sustainable Living and Peace Centre
South West England
eco-architectureandplanning.com

Vivarium Trust
Scotland
www.vivariumtrust.co.uk

The Diggers & Dreamers Reviews

Cohousing in Britain

Bunker et al (eds), 163 pp
£12, ISBN: 978-0-9545757-3-1

The history, current practice and potential of cohousing – a form which combines the benefits of individual homes with those of communal living. A bottom up initiative with people coming together to finance, design, build and run their neighbourhood. Private homes sit alongside facilities such as a common house for regular meals and events, a laundry, guest rooms and even car pools and workshops.

Low Impact Living Communities in Britain

Bunker et al (eds), 152 pp
£12, ISBN: 978-0-9545757-4-8

Human impact on the Earth has to be reduced but how far are you prepared to go? Could you live a really low impact lifestyle? Would it be easier if you were within some type of low impact living community? These groups exhibit ground-breaking inventiveness and ingenuity and there are lessons here for everybody who wants to carry on enjoying life on this lovely planet.

Historical Books from D&D

Utopia Britannica:
British Utopian Experiments
1325–1945

Chris Coates, 312 pp

£16.50, ISBN: 978-0-9514945-8-5

Travel through utopian Britain.
Move through a country of the
imagination dreamt into
existence by generations of
utopian experimenters who
refused to accept that there
wasn't a better place to be
than the one that they
found themselves in.

Communes Britannica:
A History of Communal
Living in Britain 1939-2000

Chris Coates, 520 pp

£25, ISBN: 978-0-9514945-9-2

This myth-busting tour by a
veteran communard takes you
from war-time pacifist land groups
right through to hippie communes.
It shows that communal living
actually provided a viable way of
life for thousands in the latter half
of the twentieth century.

The Editors

James Dennis aka The Forest, born 1980. Doing his best to follow a path to contentment which seems to involve hiding with Bruce Chatwin – his dog – in the Scottish Highlands (pretending to be a barman) while he gets over being too poor to be a peasant. He lived at Redfield for four years and is perhaps the UK's foremost community-spotting anorak, having visited about 80 places since 2008. He initiated a Transition Group, has 105% vision, likes Jung, was once shot in the head, is in love with several women and has a rare tropical disease named after him... one of those things is a lie.

Chris Coates, born 1957. How many hats ca man wear? Squatter turned eco-housing develo Utopian student and chronicler of commu history; former Lancaster Green Party counci fringe actor-cum-street-clown; writer; carpen timber framer; general builder; director of that and the other; caretaker; veteran commun (25 years and counting); bonfire builder; Engir of the Imagination; project manager; birdwatc cultural activist; father; son; brother; friend and lo Give that man a hat sta

Sarah Bunker, born 1964. Bunk was inspired by Sunseed in Spain to live communally, and she joined Beech Hill Community in 1989, where she lived for 16 years, completing a science PhD, constantly patching up the crumbling buildings along with fellow communards, growing veg and swimming naked whenever possible! She joined the D&D collective in 1996 and retired in 2013. She is living with her partner just down the road from the Beech Hill Mothership dreaming of a lightweight, energy-efficient, low-maintenance mobile home community somewhere in Cornwall.

Jonathan How, born 1953. A member of Redf Community for 13 years from 1984. Now live a little house by himself at the UK's south-wes extremity but remains as interested as eve utopias. Believes that communal living may no for everyone but that the significance of intentic communities is that they can act like hot-houses new ideas. The bond between fellow communar a kind of new hybrid between neighbour and fa member – is a prime example. It's just the kin thing that's very much needed in the wider wo

Lightning Source UK Ltd.
Milton Keynes UK
UKHW022134080519
342347UK00010B/35/P